D1458857

MAJOR THOMPSON LIVES IN FRANCE

and

MAJOR THOMPSON AND I

Major Thompson Lives in France
and
Major Thompson and I

PIERRE DANINOS

with drawings by Walter Goetz

THE REPRINT SOCIETY LONDON

Major Thompson Lives in France FIRST PUBLISHED 1955
Major Thompson and I FIRST PUBLISHED 1957
THIS COMBINED EDITION PUBLISHED BY THE REPRINT SOCIETY LTD.
BY ARRANGEMENT WITH JONATHAN CAPE LTD. 1959

PRINTED IN GREAT BRITAIN
BY RICHARD CLAY AND COMPANY, LTD., BUNGAY, SUFFOLK

CONTENTS

MAJOR THOMPSON LIVES IN FRANCE

Contents
MAJOR THOMPSON AND I

ILLUSTRATIONS

MAJOR THOMPSON LIVES IN FRANCE

A 2

Illustrations

MAJOR THOMPSON AND I

MAJOR THOMPSON
LIVES IN FRANCE
and Discovers the French

MAY I INTRODUCE MYSELF?

No well brought up Englishman (if I may be allowed the use of such a pleonasm without shocking my honourable countrymen) can, without loss of dignity, talk about himself, especially at the beginning of his story. But, like astronauts who when they reach a certain height are no longer subject to the laws of gravitation, once I am landed on the Continent, I no longer feel bound by the laws of British gravity. And since I shall have to speak about themselves to people to whom I have never been introduced, I feel freer to do what isn't done and give details about myself which on the other side of the Channel would seem uncalled for.

My name is Thompson.

William Marmaduke Thompson.

Having had the good fortune to be born an Englishman I go forward in life like a sandwich-man, preceded by my initials and followed by the little cushion whereon national honours with the passing of the years have added their alluvial deposit C.S.I., D.S.O., O.B.E.

It is unbelievable how precious these letters fore and aft are to an Englishman: they are the inviolable frontiers of his person, protecting him like a ceremonial waterproof from too direct human contacts. When a Frenchman sends me a letter addressed 'Monsieur Thompson' I feel as if I'd caught a cold in my surname and been undressed in public, which is annoying: for after all, it is the sender who is in the wrong and I who feel I am giving offence.

I should be sorry for the French to take this remark amiss. If I venture to talk about them frankly it is because I love them every bit as much as they love the Queen of England: could anyone love them more than that? After I came out of the Army and

Ursula had passed away,[1] I made my home in Paris, in the country of my second wife, so that I feel doubly privileged: I'm an Englishman nourished *à la française*.

The many sports on the fringes of which I pursued my studies (without ever seeming to catch them) did not develop me physically any more than is usually the case with my country-men. I am fairly tall, and highly coloured in complexion: the slight parenthesis of my legs betrays the horseman. My eyes are blue and round, and a state of perpetual astonishment (especially since I've lived in France) makes them look prominent and ready to jump out of their sockets; my nose stops short and looks as if there hadn't been time to finish it, my plump cheeks shine like Canadian apples and their ruddiness, together with the bluish line of my temples, and the white bar of my moustache make up a living reminder of the Union Jack.

When I add that my front teeth, which are slightly projecting and rest visibly upon my lower lip, make the unsuspecting (not in England where this malformation is pretty common) believe that I am always laughing and am even more jovial than my com-plexion would lead them to think, I shall have shamefully misused my pen to draw my own portrait.

But I must get down to speaking of the chief cause of astonish-ment in my life, which is the subject of these notes.

Now I know this will appear incredible, and yet it is the un-varnished truth: India's sun has tanned my skin; for the safety of Her Most Gracious Majesty I have roasted in the burning sands of Mesopotamia; the Intelligence (which in Great Britain is more keenly appreciated as a branch of the Services than as a quality) sent me to live in the execution of very confidential missions in Bechuanaland, in Palestine, and among the Afghans. And yet I may say today that never have I felt so far from home as now, twenty-one miles from Dover, in this fair land which bears the delectable name of France.

May the elongated beasts on the Royal Standard tear me to

[1] Expression which the English prefer to the word 'die' especially when speaking of someone dear to them. Ursula was the Major's first wife.

THOMPSON, MAJOR HON. WILLIAM MARMADUKE, C.S.I.
(1934), D.S.O. (1943), O.B.E. (1931). *b.* 8 oct. 1902. 4th *s.* of
Earl Strawforness. *Education*: Rugby; Trinity College, Oxford.
Married: 1. 1929 Penelope Ursula Hopkins († 1931); 2. 1932
Martine-Nicole Noblet. Entered Army 1924, served Waziristan
Campaign (1924), transferred to India, Rawalpindi District
(1926), 9th Lancers Mesopotamia (1928), 38th Dogras Palestine
and Egypt (1931). Secretary to the Hon. the Political Resident,
Persian Gulf (1931). Political Agent, Kuwait (1932). Served
2nd World War 1939–1945 with Royal Warwickshire Regt.
(despatches twice, D.S.O., Croix de Guerre). Retired from
army 1945. Member H.M. Diplomatic Service. *Publication*:
The Arab of Mesopotamia; various communications on the South
African lepidoptera. *Recreations*: big-game hunting, natural
history, golf, gardening. *Clubs*: Cavalry (London), Automobile
Club (Paris), Honourable Company of Edinburgh Golfers
(Muirfield). *Addresses*: England: Tower Cottage, Rowlands
Castle, Pendleton, Hampshire. Continent: c/o Thos. Cook and
Son, Paris.

bits if I am lying: I feel nearer to London in the Caiman Islands
than in Angoulême, and the customs of the Maori warriors seem
to me less mysterious than the habits of a burgher of Roubaix.[1]
So true is it that the Almighty needed only a few pailfuls of water
to separate the two most dissimilar peoples in the world.

Briefly then, at a time when the whole world appears to be
caught up in the vertigo of exploration, and obnubilated by the
heights of the Himalayas or depths of the Pacific, it seems to me
more than ever urgent to discover France.

P.S. I owe my thanks for his meritorious efforts to my friend
and collaborator P. C. Daninos who is so grieved he isn't
English—that would have been his only chance of acquiring
some sense of humour: as it is he is reduced to translating my
thoughts. *Traduttore traditore.* May he never betray me! That
is what I hope for but can scarcely believe. When people have
been hereditary enemies for so long, something always remains
in the subconscious (I saw that by his remarks about Calais).
And then, believe it or not, though he has been speaking English
for only twenty years he thinks he knows it. It would be equally
presumptuous on my part to claim that because I have been
meeting French people for a quarter of a century, I know them.
The only people who claim to know such a country inside out
are those who have spent a fortnight going through it, and have
left with a ready-made opinion in their suit-case. Those who *live*
there learn every day that they know nothing about it except
perhaps the opposite of what they already knew.

[1] The Major had first written 'Calais'. But I pointed out to him that the name
coming from an English pen was ill chosen, since the six nightshirts of the roped-
together burghers still flutter ineffaceably in the sky of History. The Major agreed:
'Come to think of it, "Roubaix" is better.'

WHAT IS A FRENCHMAN?

IN the secrecy of his Harley Street surgery a friend of mine, a famous brain surgeon, one day opened up an Englishman. And he discovered: first, one of Her Majesty's battleships, then a waterproof, a royal crown, a cup of tea, a dominion, a policeman, the rules of the Royal and Ancient Golf Club of St Andrews, a Coldstream Guardsman, a bottle of whisky, a Bible, the Calais–Mediterranean time-table, a Westminster Hospital nurse, a cricket ball, some fog, a bit of the earth on which the sun never sets, and—right at the bottom of his subconscious, lined with age-old turf—a cat-o'-nine-tails and a black-stockinged schoolgirl.

Conscious of having committed an unpardonable indiscretion, rather than appalled by his discovery, he neither called in Scotland Yard nor the Vice Squad: he sewed him up again. And he had to conclude that all those things constitute a really good Englishman.[1] I have often wondered what my friend would find if he cut open a Frenchman.[2]

How should one define a Frenchman?

The accepted definition of the Frenchman as one who eats bread, knows no geography and wears the Legion of Honour

---

[1] The Translator, at the risk of shocking certain purists by turns of phrase which are anglicisms and not French, has been anxious as far as possible to retain the aroma, he might say the *flavour*, of Major Thompson's text by keeping to the literal translation.

[2] A South African girl, having read about the Major's problem in her newspaper, wrote to the *Natal Daily News* of Durban which published on 20th January 1954 this curious reply: 'I know the surgeon in question and can confirm the Major's statement; I was the nurse, and saw the different objects brought out. What the Major does not relate is that the surgeon was French, and what he does not know is that I fell in love with him. One day he himself underwent a brain operation. To the general amazement, when his skull was opened there were found nineteen ex-Presidents of the Council, three dancers from the Folies Bergère, half a box of ripe Camembert, an absolutely complete Maginot Line, and several lorry loads of devalued francs.'

in his buttonhole, is not inaccurate (although the Legion of
Honour when you look more closely is the Order of Ouissam
Alaouite).

But it doesn't go far enough.

I am alarmed by the thought [1] that if my friend were to cut
open a Frenchman he would fall dizzily into an abyss of contra-
dictions.

Really . . . how can you define these people who spend their
Sundays proclaiming that they are republicans and the rest of the
week worshipping the Queen of England, who call themselves
modest yet always talk about being custodians of the torch of
civilization, whose common sense is one of their principal exports, while they keep so little of it for themselves that they
overthrow governments almost before they are set up, who keep
France in their hearts and their fortunes abroad, who are enemies
of Jews in general but intimate friends of some particular Jew,
who love to hear their comedians make fun of retired army
officers but who brace up at the slightest bugle call, who hate to
have their failings exposed but constantly speak ill of themselves,
who say they love pure lines but cherish an affection for the
Eiffel Tower, who admire the Englishman's ignorance of
'Système D' [2] but would think it absurd to declare the correct
amount of their incomes to the Inland Revenue, who revel in
stories of Scotch meanness but will always try to buy at a price
below the marked figure; who refer complacently to their
History but don't want any more *histoires*, who loathe crossing a
frontier without smuggling some little thing but dislike not
keeping the rules, who are anxious to proclaim that you can't
take them in but rush to elect a deputy who promises them the
moon, who say 'ne'er cast a clout till May is out' but cut off the
heating at the end of March, who vaunt the charms of their
countryside but let their builders cover it with architectural eye-

---

[1] A turn of phrase belonging to the same category as the famous 'I'm afraid' so
dear to the English: for example, when an Englishman knows quite well that he
has forgotten something, he says he is very much afraid he's forgotten it. And if a
woman who has just seen her husband set off for his office has to answer a 'phone
call for him, she will generally say 'I'm afraid he's out.'
[2] The Art of wangling.

AT *MON REPOS*: THE FRENCHMAN'S DREAM OF RETIREMENT

sores, who have a marked respect for the law courts but go to a
lawyer only to find out how to get round the law and, finally,
who are delighted when a great man talks to them of their *greatness*, their *great* civilizing mission, their *great* country, their
great traditions, but who dream of retiring after a pleasant
little life, into a quiet *little* corner, on a *little* piece of ground
of their own, with a *little* wife who will be content with in-
expensive *little* dresses, concoct for him nice *little* dishes and on
occasion invite his friends charmingly to have a *little* game of
cards?

These conservatives who for the last two hundred years cease
not to slip to the left until they there rediscover their 'right',
these republicans who for more than a century have repressed
their royalism and taught their children with tears in their
eyes the history of the kings who created France—how can
a poor devil of an observer define them except in terms of contradiction?

A Frenchman? A being who above all is the opposite of what
you think he is.

Admitting that, if I must try to determine the dominant
feature of their characters, I would say it is: scepticism.

My old friend M. Taupin says he is much attached to the
republican institutions, yet, if a deputy ends up his speech with
an appeal to the great principles of 1789, he smiles ironically. It
is clear he no longer believes in them. M. Taupin is a convinced
partisan of peace. Yet when the representatives of the Great
Powers meet round a piece of green baize to try and lay what the
press-architects call the foundations of a world agreement, and
then publish a communiqué which proves the *identity of their
points of view*, he smiles again, shakes his head and says:

'You don't mean to say you believe *that*? . . . Words, words,
words, nothing but words! . . .'

Invaded, occupied, oppressed, bullied, trailing behind him the
regrets of 1900 and the gold standard, M. Taupin is a man who
doesn't believe in anything because in his opinion it no longer
serves any purpose to believe in anything.

After the English have waited a long time they do something. Since they don't think much, and reflect even less, they do believe in doing something.

The French don't believe in what they do. Take the Chamber of Deputies.

It looks as if they manufactured deputies just for the pleasure of destroying them. If I go with M. Taupin in a 'bus past the Chamber his face lights up in a sarcastic smile.

Is he a royalist? No.

Bonapartist? Not that either.

Does he long for a dictatorship? He has a horror of it. So what?

He is a moderate whose revolutionary spirit is confined to making him vote radical, or, if he is in a really bad temper, radical-socialist. Perhaps just as our 'bus is passing the Chamber, the very member elected by M. Taupin is invoking the sacred principles of 1789 and the Rights of Man. And yet he doesn't believe in them, doesn't believe in them any longer. M. Taupin declares that a man is not the same man once he has taken his seat with six hundred others. Perhaps he is right. In any case it is clear that he regards his representatives with little goodwill, rather with that eye we turn on a usurper who dares to sport a black tie with narrow blue stripes when he has never been to Eton. And it's plain from their expressions that his neighbours think as he does. It is hard to believe that it was the men travelling in the 'bus who sent to the Chamber the members who sit there. They seem to inhabit two different planets.

Generally the situation is summed up by a gentleman wearing a decoration:

'What we need is a strong man who would clear things up a bit in there . . . make a clean sweep.'

You might suppose the people wanted a dictator. Wrong. Let the strong man appear on the horizon, speak of reforming institutions, restoring order, establishing discipline, and for one satisfied voter you have a thousand malcontents. He is called a traitor. He wants to butcher the Republic. *Ils ne passeront pas!* They shan't get through! 1789 is invoked, and this date, which only a moment ago made M. Taupin laugh, now makes him very serious.

An impartial observer might be tempted to believe that what the French have most at heart is universal suffrage, the expression of the will of the people, republican institutions, in a word the Chamber. But you have only to pass by in a 'bus . . . (see above).

It is easy to see that, given these conditions, France is a difficult country to govern. Power slips out of hands as soon as they have grasped it. Yet foreigners are wrong to criticize the French from this point of view and accuse them of inconstancy. In my view it is a sign of good health. Many countries lose their heads because they lose their governments. The French, whose governments are certainly enough to make them lose their heads, have the incomparable virtue of keeping calm on these occasions. France is the only country in the world possessing a body which is healthy enough to allow her to live, for one month out of every four, without a head. With us a government is a necessity; in France it is a luxury which she can offer herself three, four or five times a year thanks to the soundness of her constitution and her famous common sense, which enables this admirable nation to venture without losing its balance along the most damnably difficult paths.

SWEET LAND OF MISTRUST—AND CREDULITY

THE French are inclined to believe that other countries live with their eyes fixed on France. At least that's what their newspapers say. At the slightest crisis they write: 'Every day the foreigner is watching us.'

I must say it is rare for me to take my stand on the cliffs of Dover before daybreak to watch through a telescope how the French set about getting up! [1] I think it would be indecent. Still—no doubt some damned foreigners spend all their time in such a way.

I used to wonder about this inquisitive foreigner, then I saw him in one of my rare dreams. He had one foot in the Kremlin, the other in the City, his head was British, his stomach Russian, his subconscious German, his wallet American, his memory stuffed with Waterloos and Sedans. He was watching Fair France with an international, slightly malevolent eye.

The French are convinced that their country wishes harm to no one. The English are condescending, the Americans bossy, the Germans sadistic, the Italians incomprehensible, the Russians impenetrable, the Swiss Swiss. But the French are nice. And other people are horrid to them.

There are two possibilities for France.

To dominate the world by her radiance (territorial conquests, development in Arts and Letters, etc.)—these are the great heroic epochs of radiant France. Or to be invaded and conquered. Then France is trodden underfoot, massacred, crucified. These are the great heroic epochs of humiliated France.

[1] In French: *Se lèvent.* The Major had first written *se lavent* (how they wash) but his collaborator pointed out that the French might see herein a hurtful allusion to recent statistics which revealed that the French use in a year only half as much toilet soap as the English do. 'Of course,' agreed the Major, '*se lèvent* but it's even more *shocking*.'

The first condition satisfies France's pride and thirst for greatness—the Napoleonic side. From the second she draws her
irresistible force of recovery—the Joan of Arc side.

It is difficult for a Frenchman to imagine that anyone can
honestly see France otherwise than olive-branch in hand, a gentle
prey at the mercy of bellicose nations. Any honest observer
must admit that this state of mind is fairly legitimate, since three
times in less than a century France has had to suffer the most
savage onslaughts of the Teuton races. Still, if he can get into
the right perspective for an impartial judgment and, disregarding
the records of the last eighty years (mere grains of dust in
History's hour glass), study the annals of earlier centuries, he
must admit that a Spaniard whose town was sacked by Napoleon's armies finds some difficulty in considering France as an
innocent victim. Foreigners should, however, realize that when
a French army goes into the Palatinate or into Saragossa, it
doesn't do it on purpose.[1]

Persecuted by her enemies who make war, by her allies who
make peace behind her back, by the whole world which steals
her inventions (the French invent only to complain the next
minute that the invention has been stolen), the Frenchman also
feels persecuted by the French: by the government which makes
a fool of him, by the Treasury which makes him pay too many
taxes, by his chief who pays him too little for his work, by
business men who make fortunes at his expense, by his neighbour
who slanders him—in short by anybody.

This state of continual menace in which he believes he is
cornered mobilizes him into a permanent condition of self-
defence. That comes out clearly when two Frenchmen ask after
each other. In other countries people are getting on well, or
badly, but anyhow getting on. In France 'they defend themselves'.

---

[1] This passage brought about a lively discussion between the Major and his
French collaborator. 'Am I to understand that if your revered ancestor Major
Raikes Hodson, in the name of His Most Gracious Majesty, with his own hand puts
to death the three sons of an Indian potentate and sends their father to die in
exile at Rangoon, it's all for their good?' 'In a way, yes, definitely,' said the
Major.

The average Frenchman's 'I'm doing as well as I can' is the mark of a man who is perpetually on the defensive.

Yet who attacks the nice kind Frenchman? A very short word in his vocabulary to which my friend and collaborator was good enough to draw my attention disclosed the secret identity of the assailants: it's *They*. And *They* are simply everybody: the bosses for employees, employees for bosses, servants for their masters, and masters for servants, motorists for pedestrians or pedestrians for motorists, and for all of them the great common enemies, the State, the Exchequer, the Foreigner.

Surrounded by enemies even as England is by water, harassed by insatiable adventurers who envy them their lovely country, their purses, their freedom, their rights, their honour, their wives, it's easy to see that the Frenchman must be always on guard.

He is mistrustful.

Could I say he is born mistrustful, grows up mistrustful, marries mistrustfully, makes a career in mistrust and dies even more mistrustful, because, like timid people who sometimes have fits of audacity, he has from time to time been the victim of destructive fits of credulity? I think I could.

What exactly is the Frenchman mistrustful about?

From the moment he sits down in a restaurant M. Taupin—who lives in the country which eats the best food in the world—begins being mistrustful of what is 'on'. Oysters, yes.

'But,' says he to the waiter, 'are they really good? You guarantee them?'

I've never yet heard a waiter answer, 'No, I can't recommend them!' He might be heard to say, 'They are good . . . but . . . (and he leans confidentially over his customer) . . . not your sort, M. Taupin, or M. Deletange-Delbet, or M. Dupont'—which of course, especially if M. Taupin has a friend with him, sets him apart in a flattering manner.

M. Taupin knows very well that if oysters figure on the menu, it is because they are fresh, but he likes to be reassured, and above all he doesn't want to be mistaken for a man who can be taken for a ride.

CHECKING THE BILL

M. Taupin mistrusts even the water. He calls for fresh water as if there were carafes of warm or polluted water, and he wants fresh bread, and wine that isn't corked.

'Is your Pomerol decent? Drinkable? Not just some red biddy?'

Good Lord! What would happen in a country like mine where sitting down to a meal is such a horrible adventure!

Having had a good (little) meal M. Taupin does some mental arithmetic over the bill.

'It's the principle,' he says and because he doesn't want to be done. If he doesn't find a mistake he seems disappointed, if he spots one he is furious. After all that, he leaves, more mistrustful than ever.

Some time ago when I was going with M. Taupin to the Austerlitz Station (you have to go there if you want to get to the little town in the South-West we were making for), he said he must stop at a chemist's to get some medicine.

'Too bad—don't you feel well?' I asked.

'It isn't that, but I'm suspicious of the Gascon food.'

'Couldn't you buy your medicine when you get there?'

'You never know in those little towns. I shall feel more comfortable if I buy it in Paris.'

I was surprised to find that we went past a lot of chemists that looked like quite good chemists but M. Taupin seemed to have no faith in them. And then I understood the meaning of that phrase which had always puzzled me: 'On sale at all good chemists.' Those we had passed were evidently the others.

At last he found a good one. As he came back to the taxi clasping a small bottle he said apologetically: 'I mistrust all these remedies which really serve no purpose. But my wife believes in them. By faith are we saved.'

As we approached the station M. Taupin seemed anxious and kept on looking at his watch. In the end he asked the driver for *the right time*. An Englishman or a German says: 'What's the time?' 'Wieviel Uhr ist es?' And you tell him the time. But M. Taupin wouldn't be satisfied with any old time. He wants the right time—Greenwich time, Observatory time, Mt Palomar time.

On this occasion he seemed reassured by the taxi time though it
was scarcely different from his own. But when at the station he
had to make a final verification in the yard because, as he explained to me, clocks outside stations are always kept three
minutes faster than those inside, to hurry up the travellers. So
M. Taupin set his watch three minutes behind station time and a
minute fast as a matter of principle which in the end made it lose
sixty seconds.

We settled into two corner seats. Then we got out and
walked up and down the platform, but first he kept three seats
with his hat, his umbrella and my mackintosh.

'There are only two of us,' I said.

'It's safer,' he said. 'People are so pushing!'

I thought M. Taupin felt all right about the train: he had
consulted the indicator. But catching sight of an official he
inquired:

'We don't change do we? You're sure?' and turning to me,
'Those indicators! I mistrust them.'

There's nothing like a train for bringing out this *They* hydra.
I expected that, but this time I had more than I could take. The
monster seemed to be in a state of torpor in the general somno-
lence, when suddenly, at the end of this dark cold day, the electric
light failed.

'They might at least,' piped a little old lady of seventy with a
foot warmer, 'inspect their compartments before putting them
into service.' Up till then the five other French people in the
compartment, taciturn, mistrustful and reserved, had been
quietly reading their newspapers or their fellow travellers'.
(*May I? . . . Thank you so much!*) No doubt they were only
waiting for a signal—or rather the *They* sign—to dash into the
fray. Like a rugby football the *They* was at once captured by a
prosperous looking woman heavily veiled and nursing a little
dog ('*And to think they made me take a ticket for this poor little
animal!*') only to be caught in flight and converted into a try by
the right wing, a gentleman very sure of himself travelling under
the protection of the Legion of Honour rosette, gold watch and

chain, and triple chin, all of which heaved up and down with his sardonic laughter.

'So long as we pay!'

'To hell with everything else!'

The battle had become general. An old sporting instinct made me regret not taking part in it. But in my role of dumb referee I merely checked the score and counted the *Theys*.

'If we had a government——'

'There is one but it's just as if there wasn't.'

'What we need is a government which governs.'

'You're asking too much!'

'A man with a firm hand.'

'I'd turn them all out—a good old clean up!'

'Still, for the moment there they are!'

'Yes, and they mean to stay!'

'All they think of is filling their pockets!'

'Grease for the palm! Jobs for the boys!'

'And journeys paid for by the state. . . . Did you see about that so-called parliamentary mission to Darkest Africa? . . . Who pays for all that, I ask you?'

'We do!'

'You do!'

'I do!'

'But of course! It's a bit much! Shameful! What a country!'

'So rich!'

'And only asking to get on with the job!'

'They'll end by ruining it.'

'They're quite capable of that!'

'Look at this compartment! Isn't it a scandal? When I think of foreigners travelling! What must they think?' (All eyes are turned towards me, asking for pardon—'England, forgive us!')

'I shall write to the Company.'

'You can write—they won't even read your letter.'

As the Ticket Inspector happened to be passing at that moment the lady with the little dog attacked him:

'It's a scandal, do you hear, a scandal! You ought to refund my ticket money!'

'If you have a claim to make, Madam,' says the Inspector, 'you must write to the S.N.C.F.'

'Then you, what are you for?'

'I look after the tickets, Madam—your ticket, please.'

The gentleman with the Legion of Honour, who was dying to intervene, threw himself into the fray:

'I must ask you to be civil to the lady!'

'I am civil, sir, and anyway who asked you? Your ticket, please!'

'I won't show it!'

'We'll see about that—if you're trying it on.'

'That's enough of that! You'll pay for that, my friend.[1] First of all'—pulling out a gold pencil on a chain—'let me have your number.'

He drew himself up to the level of the Inspector's head, settling his spectacles and licking his pencil:

'Three thousand nine hundred and eighty-seven. Good! Well, 3987 loses nothing by waiting. Here's my ticket . . . with more to come, lots more!'

The Inspector smiled, quite calm, and click-clack, punched the ticket.

'He who laughs last laughs best,' said Mr Rosette.

'Meanwhile, tickets, please!'

Grumbling, the travellers unwillingly complied. When the Inspector had gone the lady with the dog hissed through her veil:

'Tss! What a mentality! You never saw it before the War! And they're all the same!'

'Oh, worse, Madame!'

'It just shows you!'

A few moments later when I went out into the corridor to get some air, I heard the Inspector tell his mate who had just joined him:

'I don't know what's the matter with them all today. I wouldn't touch them with the clippers.'

[1] When a Frenchman calls another Frenchman 'my friend' it's a sure sign they're already enemies. (*Major's note.*)

Inspectors mistrustful of travellers, travellers mistrustful of inspectors, who in this French train, this train of mistrust was most mistrustful?

I was still wondering when we arrived at our destination. Need I say that M. Taupin appeared mistrustful enough once he got to the hotel, especially about the beds. He poked them, felt the sheets, inspected the wardrobe. I don't think this mistrust was peculiar to him. Millions of Frenchmen are mistrustful of hotel-keepers, bills, oysters, women who lead them by the nose, army men who push them forward, politicians who hold them back, anti-militarists who would sell France to the first comer, schoolmasters who stuff the minds of their children, their enemies, their friends and, secretly, themselves.

THE REALM OF SUBDIVISION

MANUALS of Geography and Dictionaries tell us, 'the population of Great Britain is forty-nine million souls', or 'the inhabitants of the U.S.A. total one hundred and sixty million'.

They ought to say 'France is divided into forty-three million Frenchmen'.

France is the only country in the world where if you add ten citizens to ten citizens you haven't made an addition—you've made twenty divisions.

It would be much more in Freud's line than an English major's to show why it is that these guillotiners of kings, who are everlastingly divided amongst themselves, dream of Buckingham Palace and of National Union as the one panacea for all the wounds of mutilated France. Only a war can produce that prescription, which is then called by the name of Sacred Union. The French at once call up a hundred and fifty divisions. We can't complain about that. No longer able to fight with one another, they fight the common enemy, and allow us, the English, time, according to our traditions, to *wait* a little longer and *see* a little more.

As soon as peace returns France reverts to the old conflict. In the shade of the pediments preaching Equality and Fraternity she freely flings herself into one of her favourite sports—perhaps after bicycling the most popular of all—class warfare. Not wishing to compete with the experts I'll leave it to them to explain the evolution of this sport throughout the ages, its rules and its trends. One thing, however, does strike me: the American pedestrian who sees a millionaire going past in a Cadillac dreams secretly of the day when he will be driving in his; the French pedestrian who sees a millionaire going past in a Cadillac dreams

The Realm of Subdivision

The Realm of Subdivision

31

of the day when he'll get him out of it and make him walk *comme les autres*.[1]

As for enumerating all the subdivisions of Frenchmen, I give it up. But here's a pointer: for one Frenchman who wakes up in Port-de-Bouc and decides to become a nudist, you may be perfectly certain that another Frenchman arises as an anti-nudist in Malo-les-Bains.

You might think the antagonism would stop there. Not a bit. The nudist founds a society which elects an Honorary President (himself) and a Vice-President. Then the Vice-President, having quarrelled with the aforesaid President, forms a neo-nudist Committee rather more leftish than the first one. On his side the anti-nudist taking the chair at an Honorary Committee . . . etc.

The same process holds good for politics as for skiing. The fashion for short skis has just been launched. At once all skiing France has splintered into anti-short and anti-long. In the heart of every Frenchman there slumbers an *anti* ready to awaken at the approach of the mildest *pro*. This explains the inextricable puzzle of French political groups. How can a normally constituted Englishman, that is to say one just capable of understanding the difference between Conservative and Labour, appreciate all those essential shades which separate a Republican Left from a Republican of the Left, or a deputy of the *Union républicaine et d'action sociale*, from a deputy of the *Action républicaine et sociale*? Really I can't.

As I am incapable of examining the hundreds of thousands of divisions of Frenchmen (who, as we well know, hate hair-

[1] In French in the text. (*Translator's note.*) A favourite expression with the French generally followed by the word *Attendez*. Continually hearing this *Faites comme tout le monde* one might believe that in France everyone does behave like everyone else. But there's no country in the world where everyone seems so desperately anxious not to do as everyone else does, nor where people so thirsting for equality are so enamoured of favours, jumping the queue, complimentary tickets, etc.

It will be noticed that the Major carefully avoids speaking of the English pedestrian who is, of course, too well bred to dream about anything in the street.

B

splitting), I will content myself with studying the difference which daily divides France into two camps: officials who tell you that they are always the last to be considered and are always played a dirty trick; non-officials who claim that all the trouble is caused by the officials.

The result is that every day except Sunday—day of truce when the French frankly confess that they are frankly bored— forty-two million citizens are arrayed against the forty-third.

At first sight this numerical inferiority seems to condemn the officials. But you must never judge things at first sight in France. Fresh mysteries are always coming to light. In the end you understand why these people are so incomprehensible.

The citizen who ventures into a police station or a savings bank or a Town Hall puts me in mind of a bowman setting out for the Hundred Years War. Armed with ill-temper and equipped with sarcastic repartee, he is quite certain in advance that he won't get his way, that he will be sent from Bureau 223 on the mezzanine floor to guichet B on the third floor, from the third floor to the police station, from the police station to the Prefecture, where he learns that a new by-law dispenses with the necessity for producing the certificate he thought he had to have in favour of a new one which is the same as the old one only it requires fresh formalities.

Vis-à-vis this assailant, to whom the administrative vocabulary, as if anxious to put him at a disadvantage from the start, gives the name of applicant, is the official employee, generally swathed in a dim sort of overall and a suit he only puts on because he wants to wear it out.

Against the wall of this indifference (*I've seen others—if you think you're the only one. I don't make the regulations*) the arrows of the most bellicose and most decorated attackers become one by one ineffective. (*You'll hear from me again, my friend! I've a long arm.*) The long-armed gentleman produces from his pocket book a card with a red line across it, which no one has time to look at, but which produces its effect upon the public. The gentleman's long arm reaching over the official's little head pierces the office walls, crosses the Seine, makes its way into the office of the Minister who promptly sacks the delinquent.

Sheltered behind his grille the official maintains his calm: he has over his assailant that advantage which people seated in a café have over the passers-by. He feels all the more at home having made himself a little box (or in the case of the women officials a little basket), in which he keeps his or her belongings: scissors, knitting, buns, sweets and sometimes that little rubber stamp hunted for everywhere and foolishly sought for in its right place.

It may be because my letters are often destined for distant countries, but the stamps never amount to a round sum: the young lady tells me I have to pay 93 or 112 or 187 francs, and if she finds without too much trouble the first 50-franc and the second 30-franc stamp, she has to hunt all through a colleague's portfolio for the one to make up the sum—though she may, of course, discover it in the famous little box. I've noticed that the women in post offices have a marked predilection for old cigar boxes. Good heavens! Think what a damned long journey a box of Havanas must have taken before ending up as a workbox on the table of an assistant in the Post Office!

Sometimes the combatants are separated by sheet glass perforated at a certain height by a dozen small holes. I used to believe that these holes were made to facilitate the passage of verbal missiles. Not at all! They are so arranged that never are the mouths of employee and spluttering applicant on the same level. The opponents are therefore merely reduced to shouting a bit louder. Sometimes a small opening is arranged on a level with the head of the official. That means that the assailant is forced to lower his in a movement which at once places him in an inferior position.

Through these slits, holes or gratings, the Frenchman devotes a precious part of his existence to proving that he does exist, that he really does live where he lives, and that, since they are not yet deceased, his children are alive.

You might think that if a Frenchman isn't dead he is alive. Wrong! In the eyes of the administration he is not alive. He

CIVIL SERVICE!

must first have a birth certificate, then a life certificate, sometimes both. (It's true that lately the life certificate has been replaced by a certificate of non-decease. The French are decidedly fond of playing on words, even on those words it is best not to play with.)

Having proved in black and white—if one may use such funereal terms—that he is alive, the Frenchman must then prove a great deal more, if he is planning to go to Italy and needing a passport. Strange as it may appear, a Frenchman's journey to Italy begins in his concierge's lodge; the concierge can deliver to him without delay—or later on, according to the state of her temper—the 'domicile certificate' he needs. The adult Frenchman cannot himself certify that he inhabits the house he lives in. For that he must have the seal of his concierge. After that he will have plenty of time to exhume old memories while he searches for his military-service book, which is rarely in the same place as he left it in ten years ago.

Some while back I met M. Taupin on his way to the police station. He needed a new identity card. A naïve observer would imagine that as M. Taupin has been well known and respected in his neighbourhood for some thirty-five years he wouldn't need anyone to declare that he really is M. Taupin. Still wrong! M. Taupin, in order to declare who he is, must furnish two witnesses. These two witnesses would have to be people who've known him for a long time? Again wrong! The witnesses who have to say they know him do not know him at all, but they are known to the Inspector. Generally they keep the local *bistro* [1] or grocer's shop, and by a daily trade in witnessing make something on the side.[2]

Such is the charmingly frank (*à la bonne franquette*) aspect of this fair land, where a smile can soften a gendarme's heart, where

---

[1] In French in the text.

[2] There had been signs of an impending discussion between the Major and his French collaborator, and it flared up at this juncture. The latter having pointed out that the slowness of the English public services was proverbial, and official indifference there at least equal to that of their French colleagues, the Major said: Slow, I grant you. But not indifferent . . . let us say rather phlegmatic, *you know. . . .*

you can always discover a loophole in the law by which it can be evaded and where the strict application of regulations amounts to a sanction. The important thing is the formality. I realized that the minute I set foot in France at Calais, when I heard a disillusioned Customs officer with a luscious Auvergnat accent say to a traveller guilty of two infringements:

'If this happens again I'll have to enforce the Regulations.'

THE LAND OF THE HAND-SHAKE

For the French—and for many others—England is 'the land of the hand-shake'.

M. Taupin who, in spite of what I've told him a hundred times, always insists on making me sit in a draught, believes that he must shake hands with great violence because I am English and come from England, the land of the 'hand-shake'.

Actually, though the vigorous English hand-shake is a favourite gesture with French writers who set their detective stories in England to make them seem more real, I think the true land of hand-shaking is France.

Hand-shaking, in a way, is rather like table manners. The English have taught the whole world how to behave properly at meals; it is the French who know how to eat. The Anglo-Saxons have discovered a very evocative name for hand-shaking: it is the French who do the shaking. With us this faintly barbaric contact is reduced to a minimum. Once we have shaken hands with someone he need not expect anything else of this nature for the rest of his life.

A statistician in whose calculations I have the utmost confidence, since he is not a member of any Statistical Society and wisely limits his incursions to the neighbourhood of certain figures without ever attacking the figures themselves, calculates that a Frenchman of average importance, like M. Taupin or M. Charnelet, spends (roughly) half an hour a day (i.e. more than a whole year out of a life of sixty years) shaking hands: at nine o'clock, at twelve, at two and at six. That, of course, doesn't include the hands of people he doesn't know or visitors, relatives or friends—which would probably raise the annual total to three weeks of hand-shaking, say, three years out of a life-time. When we consider that this hand-shaker spends (roughly) three hours a day at table and eight in bed, we must conclude that the

Frenchman *lives* (in the English, i.e. correct, meaning of the word) only thirty years out of sixty, which isn't enough! [1]

With us this business of shaking hands has been standardized for the last thousand years; with the French it has various shades: it can be warm, friendly, condescending, cold, evasive, dry. Some people believe they haven't shaken hands unless they've reduced your finger-joints to pulp. Others retain the hold on your hand as if they were loth to give it back to you— use it to emphasize their arguments before letting it drop. Some keep your hand warm between both of theirs, some again seem to insinuate a soft tepid pancake [2] into your palm, which is unpleasant. Others offer you three fingers, or two, or the tip of one. Never mind, they are offering something and you ought to take it. I often see Frenchmen perform miraculous feats of agility right in the middle of lines of traffic in order to transfer to their left hand what they were carrying in their right, and, at the risk of being run over a hundred times, give their right hand to somebody whom this attention leaves unmoved, though, occasionally, dead.

---

[1] A very stormy argument which at one moment threatened to bring their partnership to an end now arose between the all-too-galloping Major and his somewhat excited French collaborator.

'Your way of life,' said the latter, 'is simply deadly!'

'The English,' retorted the Major, 'prefer to die living in that way. . . .'

'Why, then, did you come to live in France?'

'That's another story,' said the Major. 'Anyhow you must admit that the English waste less time over meals than you do.'

'They waste quite enough, when you think what's on their plates!' mused the Frenchman. 'And besides, that's not true. You take three meals a day where we only take two, and statistics prove that you absorb more calories.'

'That arises from the recognized fact that our combustibility is first class.'

'And your tea?' inquired the Frenchman.

'What about our tea?' asked the astonished Major.

'Yes, have you calculated that the Englishman who takes his early morning tea at 7 a.m., more tea at breakfast, tea in the office for elevenses, tea at lunch, tea at tea and finally a cup of tea before he goes to bed, spends (roughly) four years of his life in front of a tea-pot, which, after all, is only Chinese nonsense.'

The Major who had turned very red chose to leave the room at this juncture in order to lose his temper in comfortable seclusion. He came back an hour later, calm and having taken his refuge by ingurgitating a cup of his favourite beverage in an *English Tea-room* in the Rue de Rivoli.

[2] The Major in a desire to smooth over the recent incident made an elegant concession and actually used the French form *pannequet*.

The other evening I was watching a dramatic critic finishing off an article his paper was waiting for. Some friends came up, hesitated, then, seized with a kind of vertigo, fell upon him with outstretched hands. They couldn't help it, nor could he.

Five times in five minutes I saw him shake hands with people who said 'Please—don't get up' but who would have thought him very stand-offish if he hadn't upset all his notes and mislaid his pen in order to bid them 'Good evening'. The French are extremely touchy on this point.

Somebody would have remarked at once:

'Why, he didn't shake hands!'

'Queer!'

He would have to search all through yesterday's behaviour to discover some detail he had forgotten which may have given offence. 'He didn't shake hands with me as usual' is just as serious. The supreme affront is not to take a proffered hand but leave it suspended in mid-air. When a Frenchman says, 'I wouldn't take his hand' it's like our saying, 'I cut him dead'.

A foreigner who has lived for some time in France soon acquires the habit of grasping every hand within reach. Now, when I go back to England, my forearm is continually stretching out into the void. My compatriots don't know what to do with it. Too bad! . . . It is easy to stretch out your hand but disconcerting to have to withdraw it when nobody wants it. The other day in Grosvenor Square a sympathetic Englishman did take my hand, but, come to think of it, it was probably just by chance, or perhaps he was a foreigner.

Not for nothing, indeed, was that little strip of water which separates England from the Continent called an 'arm of the sea' or 'La Manche'. It is without doubt the frontier of the arm. Twenty-one miles of sea and a hand held out is no longer to be kissed, the arm which moved about must be kept still.

The English, from that tender age when they already appear so hardened, learn to live with their elbows close to their sides— on foot, on horseback, at table. Watch an Englishman eating.

B 2

LE HAND-SHAKE AT ALL COSTS

You can scarcely see his arms move. It looks as if he wasn't eating (and *can* he be said to eat?) but having his food delivered to his palate by the Intelligence Service. There ought to be a planisphere of gesture. It would show that the human arm, motionless at Bournemouth, begins to move about at Calais, is agitated in Paris, and whirls round frantically in Rome, where it becomes a thought-propeller.

It isn't only in their way of saying 'Good-day' that the French appear so strange to their neighbours. What follows is equally amazing.

When an Englishman meets another Englishman he says, 'How d'ye do?' and is answered, 'How d'ye do?'

When a Frenchman meets a Frenchman he says, 'Comment allez-vous?' and the other immediately begins to give him news of his health.

The British method seems perfectly crazy. On reflection it's perhaps more rational than the French. In the first case nobody listens to anybody. In the second, with rare exceptions, the Frenchman doesn't listen to the answer. Either he's in good health and cares little about the health of the other fellow, or else he's got a cold and the only thing he cares about is his own cold. For example:

'Still got my sciatica!'

'Ah! . . . sciatica! With me it's all down my left leg. In 1951 I went to a specialist—yes, another one! D'you know what he said? . . .'

And the Frenchman who is suffering from sciatica suffers still more because he has to keep quiet about his 1954 sciatica and listen to the other fellow's 1951 neuritis. It's the same when it comes to a good story, motor accident or business. The French are only interested in those things which happen to themselves and which are not interesting in other people. Of course this conversational selfishness isn't peculiar to them: one could say the same of other peoples. It would be true and it would be false. The English are as little interested in their neighbours as the French. But since they don't ask intimate questions about stomach-aches, impetigo or the liver (Private Enemy No. 1 with the French) they don't have to listen to the answer.

Having inquired after their respective healths, that of their relatives and children (Photos?—aren't they splendid!—I must show you mine!) the French pass on to the 'What are you doing now?' '*Qu'est ce que vous devenez?*' [1]

Unlike the English who never ask such an agonizing question, the French really want to know. So in one minute you must explain that you are not divorced, you haven't moved, and especially that you are—

'Still with the Crédit Lyonnais?'

'Still with the United Insurance?'

'Still with the Oil Company?'

—as if your questioner were astonished they'd kept you on so long.

After this stock-taking, during which you bewail your own bad luck and the good luck of others, it's customary to make a rapid return to the health question with, 'At all events you've got your health—that's the main thing anyway' (*allez!*).

The conversation goes on for a bit and finally ends on the no less traditional 'I must fly! *Allez, au revoir!*'

I've questioned several natives on this quasi-traditional ritualistic expression *Allez!* Nobody could explain it. I suppose it has something to do with a curious invisible means of locomotion by which a Frenchman sets off when parting from another Frenchman. Really most peculiar!

Heavens! I hear the whistle of my tea-kettle. Sweet call that even the most Francophile Englishman couldn't resist. I must go and see. And I'll leave it at that for the moment.

[1] In French in the text.

COURTEOUS OR GALLANT?

EVERY French schoolboy knows that at the battle of Fontenoy the officer commanding the French guards, M. d'Anterroches,[1] advancing alone towards the English, uncovered and cried:

'Messieurs les Anglais, fire the first shot!'

Every English schoolboy knows that at the battle of Fontenoy the officer commanding the English guards, Lord Hay, advancing alone towards the French, uncovered and cried:

'Messieurs les Français, fire the first shot!'

As for the experts—divided as they are from birth—they of course disagree. That's their job.

According to some, those words were addressed to the French by one of their leaders who, on seeing the English emerge from a peculiarly British fog, cried (with this punctuation):

'Gentlemen, the English! Fire the first shot!'

Others see here a stratagem which was classic at that time when French strategists believed it was better to let the enemy use up his first cartridges so as to attack him more easily afterwards.

[1] The Major had originally written d'Auteroche. But the Vicomte d'Anterroches, descendant of the Comte d'Anterroches, captain in the French Guards and hero of the battle of Fontenoy, pointed out to him that it was beyond doubt, first that the famous 'Messieurs les Anglais, tirez les premiers' was pronounced by his gallant ancestor and not by M. d'Auteroche, and secondly that in the eighteenth century 'since French was the language commonly spoken by persons of quality it could not have been incomprehensible to English officers'.

On the first point, the Major readily admitted that the Vicomte d'Anterroches was right, and he is supported by the Memoirs of Marshal Saxe which are authentic. For his documentation the Major had only at his disposal Voltaire's *Précis du Siècle de Louis XV*, and the testimony of eye witnesses, the Marquis de Valfons and the Chevalier de Roburent, Captain in the French Guards, and these three authors speak of Monsieur or the Comte d'Anteroche.

On the second point, the Major is more reticent and persists in believing that his distinguished compatriots didn't understand French any better in 1745 than they do now.

But many remain faithful to the classic version of this pleasing fiction, which is very French and doubly gallant.[1]

I think it only fair, however, to recall briefly the story of a French witness, the Marquis de Valfons, who wrote: 'The English officers having brought up their men to within eighty paces of the French line, halted, dressed the line and, hat in hand, saluted the French officers who in their turn uncovered.' (Extraordinary, isn't it, with what good manners they knew how to live and die in those days!)

'Then Lord Hay, cane in hand, advanced to within thirty paces of the French line, uncovered once more, and said to Count Auteroche: [2]

' "Monsieur, give the order to fire," to which M. d'Auteroche replied, "No, sir, we never begin." '

But someone must have begun, otherwise there wouldn't have been any battle of Fontenoy, which would have been just too bad for the experts. Will this honourable company allow an ex-Major in the Indian Army to give his view? In my opinion it is possible—I would not wish to cause the French any pain—that someone may have called out to Lord Hay's troops, 'Messieurs les Anglais, *tirez les premiers !*'

But it is highly improbable that anyone on the English side understood. Everyone knows that since the whole world is English-speaking, the Englishman's privilege is to understand no language other than his own. And even if he does understand in no case must he stoop to letting it be believed that he does.

An objective study of the truth leads the impartial observer

---

[1] The Major plays on the words, gallant meaning *courageux* and *galant*.

[2] The Major, anxious to respect the legitimate wishes of the Vicomte d'Anterroches, had written d'Anterroches, but a certain M. d'Auteroche, a descendant of the Comte d'Auteroche, getting on his high horse, informed him that his ancestor was certainly at Fontenoy, that there was no *a priori* proof that he had not pronounced the historic words, and that, moreover, the Marquis de Valfons spoke of the Comte d'Auteroche.

'The least that can be said,' writes M. d'Auteroche, 'is that some doubt exists as to the copyright of the famous saying.' The Major agreed and resolved never again to put his head into this hornet's nest, and finally accepted the opinion of a French expert, Othon Guerlac, who writes in a dictionary of quotations, 'The conclusion to be drawn from the divergent accounts concerning Fontenoy is that it was indeed the English who invited us to fire first.'

PASSERS-BY: FRENCH—ENGLISH

to conclude that this is merely one of those historic sayings
invented with the sole aim of helping school-children to assimilate a conspectus of synoptic dates and fables. The most durable
sayings are, of course, those which are made up all of a piece,
especially when it's a question of a piece of artillery.

In the present instance, the Fontenoy saying seems to have
emerged whole from the forges of French History which
specialize in the coldrolling of such heroic-gallant formulae as:
'All is lost save our honour', or 'Madame, if it be possible it is
done, if impossible it shall be done.'

With us the historic factories of Birmingham and Leeds,
equally renowned for coldrolling, specialize rather in a noble
simplicity: 'England expects that every man will do his duty'
(Nelson before Trafalgar), or in the satirical and haughty saying,
'I don't give a twopenny damn what's become of the ashes of
Napoleon' (Wellington), or 'What France has best taught me is
the better appreciation of England' [1] (Johnson).

Both manufacturers go ahead and compete harmlessly. Their
products are principally intended for home consumption. I have
never found the French version of Fontenoy in English school
books and I have never found a French history mentioning
Wellington's remark.

If I began by speaking of the legend of Fontenoy it's because
it so wonderfully symbolizes, if not the spirit of gallant courage
of the French, at least the spirit they would like to have. Everyone knows that in battles there's no time to pronounce these
charming sayings. The cannon speaks for the combatants. Later
on historians invent the combatants' speeches.

I should be sorry to think that anyone might see in these
remarks an attack upon historians. Every man to his trade. And
they do theirs wonderfully. My collaborator and friend, M.
Daninos, who in the last war was for some time attached as
liaison officer to my battalion, told me one day at the height of the

---

[1] The evocation of this saying occasioned a pretty lively sally between the
Major and his French collaborator, who remarked pertinently, 'One of the things
I enjoy most when I travel abroad is the thought that I am going back to France.'

retreat from Flanders how sorry he was to be in the thick of the battle. At first I thought (and it made me feel uncomfortable) that he would rather have been at home. But no. It was that as a writer he would never console himself for not being able to describe this gigantic encounter as well as his colleagues who weren't in the firing line.

That seems paradoxical, yet it's quite true. The historian, free from all the constraint which may paralyse the combatant— fear of the N.C.O., or even of the enemy—is the only one who can take the long view of the conflict, ignore all the killing of unimportant people, and impart the necessary colour and flexibility to his story.

Speaking of those who ought to be at a certain distance in order to treat their subject properly has led me to stray away from my own. To come back to Fontenoy. I'm finally inclined to believe that the 'Messieurs les Anglais, tirez les premiers' is the historic form of the very French 'After you, please'.

No, one can't consider people who don't eat keeping their elbows close to their sides, who gesticulate as they talk, talk while they're eating, or often talk about what they are eating, who, far from waiting until the ladies have left the room, hasten even with the soup to tell the most improper stories in their presence, who think they are obliged to flirt with your wife, who feel it would be rude to arrive at 8.30 when they are invited for 8.30, who kiss in public, whose men kiss each other, who never seem to finish buttoning themselves up in the streets of Paris, and hold converse with the trees when they go into the country, who never think of holding a lady's chair as she sits down at their table, who dare to call a man a murderer because he has killed four people though the police haven't yet proved it, who talk to people they don't know, especially in trains, without being forced to do so by some accident, who do not know how to brew tea, don't understand anything about cricket, try to jump the queue, who consider it a laudable feat to drive their car down a one-way street, who go out without an umbrella because it isn't raining, who in their newspapers call one of our young lords a homosexual when it would be simple to write that he

WHEN WARS WERE GENTLEMANLY—'MESSIEURS LES ANGLAIS, FI

'...T' IS THE HISTORICAL FORM OF 'AFTER YOU, PLEASE'

accosted young men, who try to pass through the automatic doors on the Métro while they're shutting, who talk about a man's mistress before mentioning his wife, who laugh about the President's feet if they're over large (and the *Présidente's* too), who use tooth-picks at table, which would not be noticed if they didn't spread out their left hands fan-wise in front of their mouths, who are much more anxious to hang up the receiver than to apologize when they get a wrong number on the telephone, who put on their best clothes on Sundays (except perhaps for a few I know in Lyons or Bordeaux who have an old Britannico-Aquitaine background)—no, as I say, one cannot consider these people are civilized or even polite, at least not in the English (i.e. correct) meaning of the word.

For a final example, take their attitude towards women. When an Englishman passes a pretty woman in the street he sees her without looking at her, never turns round and continues to see her 'correctly' in his mind. Usually when a Frenchman passes a pretty woman in the street, he first looks at her legs to see if she really is as smart as she looked; then he turns round to have a better view, and *eventually* [1] perceives that he is going the same way as she.

Polite? The French? Gallant rather! *De damnés hardis galants!* [2]

One must do them this justice: they are the champions of 'After you'—'No, after *you*'.

The French, who as we have seen devote a considerable part of their day to hand-shaking, spend also an appreciable amount of time in asking one another to come into their houses. Some beg others to enter; the others declare they won't do so. The first then say 'Nor will I'. Since the days of Charlemagne the French have spent (roughly) three and a half centuries on their doorsteps. Astonishing that we ever find any of them in their homes!

I've always found the attraction exercised by doorsteps upon

---

[1] Not *éventuellement* (i.e. suggesting some uncertainty) but finally.
[2] In French in the text.

Frenchmen rather strange. Once they reach this spot they have a way of saying goodbye without going which you find nowhere in the Commonwealth, nor perhaps in any other part of the world. At the very moment when they say they must separate after a two hours' talk, they find a lot of most important things to say. It's rather like women with the telephone: the word 'Good-bye' is a signal for the conversation to be endlessly prolonged.

I was particularly struck by this attitude when, on my return to France after a long absence on a mission in Mesopotamia, I thought I must be suffering from an hallucination. There was my old friend M. Taupin in exactly the same position as I had left him six months earlier: on his doorstep still saying goodbye to M. Charnelet. My experience in the desert had accustomed me to mirages: I couldn't believe my eyes. Discreetly I drew near. I saw M. Taupin take a few steps back, raise his arms in the air, then advance threateningly upon M. Charnelet, seize him by his coat lapels and proceed to shake him backwards and forwards. It was clear—at least to an Englishman—they were on the point of coming to blows. My Major's heart stood still; I was preparing to separate them when I heard them burst out laughing. At that moment they recognized me.

'Good Heavens!' cried M. Taupin, 'here's our Major Thompson come back! What a surprise!'

I knew then that my eyes had not deceived me. At once M. Taupin asked me in, and M. Charnelet, after saying goodbye once more, on thinking it over soon joined us for a bit of a chat. (*Un petit brin de causette.*)

THE CASE OF COUNT RENAUD DE LA CHASSELIÈRE

THE English have two possessions of outstanding value: their tweeds and their silences. The silky soft density of the first is only equalled by the noble compactness of the second. I am prepared to present ten bottles of Scotch to any explorer who discovers anywhere in the world a silence comparable to that woven by a dozen gentlemen in a St James's Street club immersed in their somnolent perusal of *The Times*.

The French, who hold that silence is golden, should therefore admit without acrimony that England is a rich country. It is, above all, in our conversation that our silence is so remarkable. That's why aliens [1] find so much difficulty in understanding us.

How the devil do the English manage to keep silence while they talk?

By their 'and—er'.

'And—er', the loom on which silent conversation, is woven is one of the oldest and most respected of British traditions. From time to time an Englishman may talk in a drawing-room. It may even happen—for anything can happen—that you meet a real talker. In that case he stops, realizes that no one is answering him except by grunts, and answers himself. A foreigner, meeting this kind of person who cuts his monologues in two, might get the impression of a dialogue. But the well-bred Englishman, that is of course any Englishman, very soon stops talking. He makes a short pause, then from the deepest caverns of his throat emerges the 'and—er'.

[1] Foreigners, but the term foreigners gives little idea of the curious sensation of uneasiness and the real inferiority complex that this word *alien* confers upon its recipient. 'So you're not a British subject, you're an *alien* . . .' and at once the visitor feels uncomfortable, set apart, suffering perhaps from some contagious disease.

With other races the 'er' implies a continuation. Not so with the English. The continuation *may* come. Generally it doesn't. What happens to it nobody knows. One thing is certain—it very rarely appears. This is the very height of reserve and discretion.

Does this mean that the English don't talk? No. Certainly they talk, but so differently from the French. In France they shine by the spoken word: the man who keeps silence commits social suicide. In England, where the whole art of conversation consists in knowing how to be silent, a man shines by his dullness.

Take for example the weather.

The French are probably past-masters in conversation but they are mere babes when it comes to the weather. That's a speciality in which the English are unrivalled. In justice to the French it must be said that they don't seek to compete with their neighbours. In France to talk about rain or fine weather amounts to a confession that one is incapable of talking about anything else. In England it is a sacred duty and the sign of a good education. To be a really good Englishman you must be able to talk about the weather—the weather we've now got, the weather we've had, the weather we may perhaps have. The word 'weather' recurs more than any other in conversation; a key word, a commanding word; weather—rainy weather, cloudy weather, dreadful weather, stormy weather, incredible weather!

Probably in the beginning of things weather was created partly to allow the English to talk about it. Really there is no country in the world where it is talked of so much. Perhaps that's why it's so bad. The impressive expenditure of meteorological terms in England every day must upset the atmosphere.

That is not the only difference between a Frenchman and an Englishman in conversation. Far from it.

In France they exaggerate the smallest incident. In England we minimize the greatest catastrophe. If a Frenchman arrives at dinner an hour late because he has mistaken the day, he'll talk all the evening about his extraordinary adventure. If an

Englishman arrives a few minutes late because the roof of his house fell in, he'll say he was delayed by a *spot of bother*.[1]

In England we never allow truth to enter our drawing-rooms naked (which is only another of the many aspects of our hypocrisy). In France only the bare truth is bearable. In England we take care not to allude in public to people's private lives. In France, on the contrary, they wallow in the details of their neighbour's home life.

I know that we are not exactly gentle. I know that our 'historical cruelty' has led us to do some very nasty things, especially in 16° south latitude.[2] I know, too, that in England as elsewhere people talk scandal, and that in general two women don't get on well together unless they are backbiting a third.

But I know nothing more cruel (if we except the customs of certain Continental nations still in a state of barbarism) than a French salon.

The only proof I will bring forward is the strange story of Count Renaud de la Chasselière.

I had been asked to dinner by some people called Pochet. There were about a dozen guests who at first talked of this and that. That is, about everything. With the soup we discussed the cinema, then we had some existentialist trout, E.D.C. with the chicken, Four Great Powers with the salad, and flying saucers with the sweet. With the French, conversation moves about with vertiginous speed. They jump from the Hydrogen Bomb to the Roland Petit ballet, from the Kremlin to the Patinos case, and all with such ease that an ex-Major in the Indian Army finds it more difficult to follow them than a tiger in the jungle of Bengal. And what marvellous shots! Goodness! Even with his Winchester 375 Magnum my friend Basil Cranworth,[3] who was

[1] That's one of the many forms of under-statement so dear to the British heart. After a night of one of the most frightful bombings of the war, Major Thompson said to me next morning, with a smile: 'We had a bit of a picnic last night.'

[2] Was the Major alluding to St Helena, or to the Boers or the Fiji Islands, all of which fall into that latitude? It was impossible to persuade him to be more precise.

[3] V.C., C.S.I., O.B.E., ex-officer in the 60th Burma Rifles.

VIVISALONSECTION: AFTER REMBRANDT

considered one of the finest shots in Assam, couldn't have brought off such results. Once caught in their fire there's no escape.

To speak of things as they are—or rather as they were, the siege of Count Renaud de la Chasselière began in the drawing-room at about 22.30 hours. At that moment the absent count was, as far as I know, still whole. All I knew about him was that he occupied an important post at the Quai d'Orsay and had conducted himself brilliantly during the war.

At 22.34 M. Pochet opened fire with, 'You know he's no more a count than I am!'—that blew off his coronet.

At 22.40 he could no longer be called de la Chasselière, it appeared he'd taken the name—and forgotten to give it back—

from a place near his estate in Sologne. His name was just
Renaud.

'And not even the *d*,' added one of the artillery, 'no—*lt !*'

'Like the four-horse-power Renault cars?' asked someone.

'Yes, that's it.'

'Well!' said the authentic Baron de Leaumes with a grimace.

The count was already badly damaged when at 22.50 a well-
informed gentleman revealed that he had only got into the Quai
d'Orsay by a fluke and never passed the Foreign Office exams.

At 22.55 a lady scored a bull by whispering that the countess
had all it takes to be a nobody.

This sly shot was followed up at once by the supporting fire
of one of the guests who hitherto hadn't fired a shot, and now
caught the enemy in the rear, so to speak, by revealing that this
father of four children had no morals at all . . . in short . . .!

I don't know what impelled me then—perhaps that old
English mania for giving a chance to the man who is down.
Inadvertently bringing the count's handicap up to its maximum
I threw out a life-buoy:

'But what about the war . . . didn't he do very well in the
war?'

'As well as everybody else . . . so what?'

We English would never have forgiven this clumsy initiative
to give the conversation another turn and I could only be sorry
that I had once again betrayed my mother tongue: silence.

At 23 hours precisely, the Count Renaud de la Chasselière fell
—wiped out.

A sad story.

Not so sad, however, if we reflect that at the same moment,
only a mile away, Count Renaud de la Chasselière with other
eminent practitioners, in the course of a similar vivisalonsection,
amputated the titles of the Baron de Leaumes, the Pochets and
several others, so that at midnight there was nothing left of any
of them.

LAWS OF HOSPITALITY AND GASTRONOMY

T HE French may be regarded as the most hospitable people in the world as long as you don't want to go into their homes.

Many foreigners intending to spend some time in France dream of living with a French family. After several unsuccessful attempts I've discovered that the best way to manage it— short of becoming a nurse *au pair*, which it must be admitted is somewhat difficult for a British major even if he wears a kilt— is to take up a position on the spot, find a French woman who will have you, and start your own family. That's what I did.

When you've met an Englishman, unless you shock him by an excess of intelligence or curiosity, at the end of an hour's acquaintance he will ask you to spend the week-end in his cottage. Five years later you'll discover that you don't really know whether he likes women, men or postage stamps.

At the end of an hour, sometimes sooner, a Frenchman will have told you how and why from time to time he is led to leave his wife, though *en passant* he assures you that she is *très gentille* —*un ange*—*mais voilà, vois savez ce que c'est* . . . (how on earth should I know?). At the end of ten years you will realize that you have never spent a night under his roof.

When I was going to Lyons for the first time, M. Taupin warned me: 'Now remember! Lyons society is very exclusive— but be patient; and when they get to know you, you'll be received everywhere.'

He was speaking only of Lyons society. I received exactly the same advice (and every time with an insistence on the purely local character of this attitude) at Bordeaux, Lille, Marseilles, and even at Mazamet. *Most important* Mazamet. You may know Pais, Roubaix, Paris, Toulouse and Carcassonne, but you won't know France if you don't know Brisbane-sur-Arnette, I mean Mazamet, capital of the sheep and woollen-stocking country. There, as elsewhere, I was told, before entering fine private houses with austere façades:

'Once they've taken you in, you'll see, you'll be one of the family!'

It's another of those vicious circles in which this country is so rich: to be received you must be known, and to be known you must be received. The chief thing with these exclusive societies is to begin to get into them. It's no good 'staying shut in outside' as they say in Limoges, when they've forgotten their latch-key.[1]

Just how long must this period of observation—I was going to say incubation—last? Impossible to say exactly. Some say six months or a year. That's a great exaggeration. It can last ten, twenty years. The best thing is to prepare for the second generation which will begin to be received, to receive and in its turn become very exclusive.

I must admit there is a great difference between the provinces and Paris.

In the provinces you are at once told, 'they're very exclusive'. You are told about the business-man from Central Europe who laid siege to Bordeaux for seven years without ever effecting a breach, or about the family from Oran which waited half a century before doors were opened to it (and which in its turn became very exclusive). In the end after all, you are received.

In Paris you are not received at all: you are taken out. The effect of the arrival of the Nicholsons or the Martinez upon their Parisian friends is really rather curious. I happened to be at the Daninoses' one day when the telephone announced the imminent arrival—I believe they spoke of the landing [2]—of the Svenssons with whom they had stayed for a fortnight in Stockholm. The

---

[1] Cf. the expression *finissez d'entrer* which the Limousins use for someone who seems to be getting congealed on the doorstep. (*Major's note.*)

[2] The Major was, alas, right.

'WHEN THEY GET TO KNOW YOU, YOU'LL BE RECEIVED EVERYWHERE'

announcement of a major catastrophe couldn't have caused more dismay.

'We shall have to take them everywhere!' I heard. Faced with the prospect of such a trial, my hosts seemed terribly tempted not to take them anywhere. The 'dinner at home with us' having been put off to a later date, the Svenssons were invited to have a drink at a café in the Champs Élysées, and in the end, after some days of gaining time, taken to one of those sanctuaries of Art and Pleasure into which Parisians rarely venture unless accompanied by a foreign mentor.

I must say, in defence of the French in general and the Daninoses in particular, that the Svenssons' appetite is colossal. I don't mean for meals (though many foreigners who at home eat practically nothing simply gorge themselves when with the French) but for buildings; Gunnar Svensson is a formidable devourer of buildings. I'd always been inclined to believe that the Swedish stomach was modelled on the same pattern as any other. Not so. They swallowed the Sacré Cœur, for example, like an hors d'œuvre.

'Now,' said Svensson, 'we must see the Catacombs.'

If the Catacombs had been in Florence, M. Daninos would doubtless have visited them three times. But since he's lived in Paris for the last forty years, he hadn't yet been there. He remembered only that one day when he was seven years old, his father said, 'If you're a good boy I'll take you on Sunday to the Catacombs'. He couldn't have been good because he never went.

My hosts tried to dissuade Gunnar. 'Wouldn't you rather go and have a drink in the Place du Tertre?' Foreigners sometimes have fixed ideas. Gunnar wanted his Catacombs. You try and make a Swede change his mind!

'That's easy,' said his host, 'I'll take you there.' It would be most annoying for a Frenchman to confess he was unacquainted with the Catacombs. It's frightful not even to know where to look for them. On the pretext of buying some cigarettes, my friend and collaborator went off for a minute and tackled a policeman: 'What's the best way to the Catacombs?' The police-

man hesitated, took out his pocket guide-book. They might
have shaken hands—as between Frenchmen.

As for hospitality, properly so-called, I believe it is easier for
an American to gain admittance to the drawing-rooms of
Buckingham Palace than to lunch with the Taupins. On arrival
he is told, 'You really must come to lunch with us. Yes, yes,
indeed you must!' Weeks go by. Something unforeseen happens, the children are ill, the cook has given a week's notice. The
Parisian ends by taking the foreigner, so avid for local colour,
to an American grill where not even the menu is printed in
French as it would be in the U.S.A.

I exaggerate no doubt. If you stay more than six months in
France you are, I admit, in the end, invited by certain families.
Then you are warned: 'You'll have to take pot luck.' Pot luck,
an emaciated affair in England, assumes in France the most
ample proportions. It explains the whole mystery: when you
take pot luck with the French and see what trouble they have
taken you realize why this 'impromptu', like that of a Member of
Parliament, must be prepared long beforehand. No hostess with
us could achieve such a result without working at it for months.
The whole question is, then, whether it is better to be invited at
once by the English or to wait six months to be invited by the
French. For my part I incline to the second answer. Good Lord!
the meal is so good that one doesn't mind having waited so long
for it.

It's not enough for their pot luck to be Pantagruelian: they
start your mouth watering with dishes that don't appear on the
table. When, freed from the constraint of British tact, I venture
to talk about what I am eating and praise the leg of lamb *à
l'anglaise*,[1] M. Taupin exclaims:

'Ah, if only you'd been here three weeks ago we'd have given
you a pheasant, oh, what a pheasant . . .!'

'Actually a hen pheasant . . . you remember, Tounet?[2] It was
plump . . . and melted in your mouth . . . and then, mind you, not
too high, just right. Oh Major! . . .'

[1] Quoted in French.   [2] Short for Gaston, pet name used by Mme Taupin.

The French have the true gourmand's way of evoking memories of good fare which enables them to enjoy feasts in words between meals. It's an incomparable pleasure for a foreigner to be their contemplative guest. On their lips the mere name of Pommard or Château Margaux emerges so rich, so velvety—already *chambré*—that you are made free at once of all the fluid treasure of Burgundy and all the secrets of the Bordeaux vines.

In this instance the pheasant—I apologize, the hen-pheasant—was there diffusing over the table the smell of game. Yet it was a leg of lamb—succulent, I must say. But with these people you soon get confused.

When a country possesses so many good things there ought not to be a close season for any of them. Only a native memory permits you to have the gastronomical calendar on the tip of your tongue. I haven't and doubtless never shall have this privilege. I realized that on my first visit to this country. When I arrived at Castelnaudary, 'You're a bit late for my little fresh livers,' said old Piquemolles. 'But I can make you a nice little *cassoulet* of preserved goose which will give you something to write home about [1] . . . You don't eat it, you suck it.' [2]

'Oh! yes, Mr Piquemolles—a nice little *cassoulet*.'

Then when I went on to the Pyrenees, 'It's a bit early for wood pigeon, Major,' said M. Cabrioules. 'What would you say to a nice little haunch of chamois?'

'Oh yes, Mr Cabrioules—a *little* haunch of chamois.'

Everywhere I went I was given good things to eat only to be made to regret I hadn't been given even better. Marvellous country, so different from my own where, because all the year round we eat the same things cooked in the same way, regret, like hope, is out of place.

---

[1] Vous m'en direz des nouvelles.   [2] Sic.

MARTINE AND URSULA

I HAVE experienced once in my life an upheaval comparable to what the earth must have suffered by the disappearance of the Hercynian forest or the crumbling of the Pillars of Hercules. It was when Martine said:

'I love those little silver threads in your moustache. . . .'

We were walking along by the Seine on one of those sunny March mornings when the pastel blue sky of the Île de France behaves like a clandestine Spring and begins its flirtation with the grey stone-work of the French Academy. I felt my world rocking; the corset of Victorian convention was bursting apart: I was falling definitely into the sentimental universe of the Latin nations. No longer was I 'Major the honourable Thompson, C.S.I., D.S.O., O.B.E.' I was about to become the husband of Martine Noblet, 'You know, that incredible Englishman with the white moustache. . . .'

Across the Channel it isn't done to speak to a man about details so personal as his moustache or the mole on his cheek. (Indeed, there are so many things that aren't done in England that the unsuspecting visitor might well believe that making love was one of them.) I had to go to France to learn—in any detail—my own geography. I mean my own personal atlas, those capes and bays and valleys which interested Ursula so little and of which Martine made such a tender and accurate survey.

Ursula would never have spoken to me in such topographical language. I still remember the expressions used when I could not bring myself to speak:

'We two . . . after all . . . What about it?'

It is after frantic declarations of this kind that English couples marry.

That's how I came to marry Ursula.

Actually it wasn't so much love that united us as a passion for horses that brought us together.

The first time I glimpsed Ursula (there are some women who should only be glimpsed) she was riding Lazy Lassie in the Dublin Horse Show. She had a way of riding at breakneck speed over this track—with its fixed obstacles one of the stiffest in the world—and of turning round in the space of a handkerchief which attracted the most uninitiated eye. The consummate skill with which she 'negotiated the oxer' [1] was even more telling. With her hunting bowler, her tight-fitting black coat, white buckskin breeches and top boots, she was a truly brave sight. The presentation of the Gold Cup gave me the chance of congratulating her. She talked of India and of pigsticking. We soon had to part but an understanding had been created, and a few weeks later, when fox-hunting had begun and I met her again out with the Quorn, we were naturally attracted to one another.

It was the end of a gorgeous autumn and the countryside and woods of Leicestershire were still resplendent in reds and golds. Whether it was due to the beauties of Nature or our Horse Show memories I can't say, but in any case we lingered and lost the hunt.

As we crossed the little village of Ratcliffe we pulled up at the Marlborough Arms for a comforting whisky or even two. Then we made our way over fields and hills, gaily jumping hedges and fences and streams. We must have been about ten miles from Brookby when, to give our horses a breather and ourselves a rest, we dismounted under the trees on the banks of the River Wreak. The silence of the countryside was broken by the sound of a furious gallop. A hundred yards away we saw a straggling horseman, who looked like the young Earl of Hertford, riding like a whirlwind over the little stone bridge. A few seconds later we heard the distant call of the huntsman and the hounds giving tongue. The hunt was a long way off.

---

[1] To 'negotiate the oxer' (or to 'negotiate the hills'), expressions favoured by English sportsmen. Certain French reporters are beginning to use the term, though Napoleon would have seen therein yet another mark of 'a nation of shopkeepers'. (*Major's note.*)

A PASSION FOR HORSES BROUGHT US TOGETHER

That day we were certainly not good sportsmen. Perhaps it had become clear to us both that there were other obstacles besides those of Dublin and Leicestershire we could tackle together. We sat down beside the water. I couldn't describe exactly what happened next; it was so sudden and extraordinary. The embrace sheltered by the noble oaks on Lord Cambleforth's estate was a compound of love, hunting and whisky in equal parts.

Why do so many women change, the moment you marry them? I was never to recapture the passionate moment that decided my fate. Everything changed from the minute I saw Ursula in a dressing-gown. I had been attracted by her 'presence', the way she moved, her distinction—all these qualities which were inseparable from the Horse Show, and which cancelled or absorbed the off-putting features—her long nose, large ears, prominent jaw. In time stable boys living night and day with horses, by some mysterious phenomenon of mimicry get to look like horses. So in Ursula there was something of the horse. When she was in riding-kit the horseface didn't matter. When we were alone together it was quite different. The amazon vanished; only the mare remained.

At first I tried to make Ursula wear, as often as possible, the rig in which I admired her. But I couldn't expect her to sleep in her bowler. No doubt my insistence seemed strange to her. From the day we went into our Hampshire home Ursula gave up riding. There was a reason for that but I only discovered it later. Her way of laughing, of joking without restraint, was quite changed. Evidently the fact that she now had to look after a house and manage servants made her more serious, more formal. She was no longer a club friend, a comrade in competitions. She was mistress of a house and much less ready to laugh at a joke than to discover traces of dust everywhere—especially from feet.

'Mind your feet, dear, when you come in. . . . Wipe your feet. . . . You've been in here again, Thompson, with your feet!'

Perhaps somewhere there exists a race of men who manage to go about without their feet. It's beyond my powers. What is certain is that our drama arose from feet. We always look for great motives for great dramas. Often they are very small even though they may be very big. Through always talking to me about feet Ursula finally forced me to look at hers. In well-made shoes most feet are passable. In a slipper Ursula's foot assumed gigantic proportions—a detail which, I may say, hadn't struck me at first because everyone said of Ursula 'She's got a good head on her shoulders'. (We ought to distrust these compliments; they so often hide something worse.)

How shall I describe—while keeping within the limits of decency—my life with Ursula?

Perhaps just in that one word—decency. This athlete, rough-rider, inveterate huntress, became metamorphosed into a paragon of decency.

'Now then. . . . Don't be sloppy, dear. Stop that nonsense. . . .' Of course all Englishwomen aren't Ursula, yet explaining Ursula helps to explain England. This kingdom ought really to have been Freud's; everything can be explained by the word inhibition. In the roystering days of Henry VIII or George IV this country was the scene of the most extravagant junketings and craziest orgies. The Victorian era set up a gigantic repression-enterprise and its disciples are still at it. Ursula was the descendant of a formidable bastion of the Victorian fortress. In Trentoran Manor where she was born, her grandmother, Lady Plunkwell, rigidly practised her Wesleyan principles: you must never mention the word legs (you must say 'extremities' or 'lower limbs'); even the piano legs were swathed in muslin.[1]

When Ursula was eleven she was sent to Meltenham School in Warwickshire, a school governed by the dual laws of monastic puritanism and sport. When she left, six years later, she may

---

[1] Today this practice is very rarely observed: but in England it is still always safer to avoid mentioning anything that lies between the chin and the knees.

not have known how a boy was made, but she herself had become one.

Once again, I am anxious to guard against generalities, but I sincerely believe that if only Englishmen could have discovered some means of bringing children into the world without having anything to do with women, they would have been the happiest people on earth. The first care in British education is to separate the two sexes as if they were never to meet again (it is true that their relationship will be limited to the minimum). While the girls are sent to institutions where their legs are encased in black stockings, and where they learn to blush for the evil sins of the flesh, and even blush at the flesh itself (at Meltenham the rule stigmatizing nudity forced the pupils to take their baths wearing a cotton night-dress), the boys are sent off to schools whence they emerge to learn with amazement that besides cricket and the Colonial Office they will, from time to time, have to think about women.

It is not enough to say that nothing is done for women. Everything is against them—themselves first of all. It is normal that a small boy's principal aim in life should be to become a man, but in the United Kingdom it is also the aim of every little girl. The mistresses at Meltenham exhorted their charges to 'Run like boys, girls, run'—which was their way of suggesting, 'That will keep you from thinking about them'. And Ursula ran like a boy, and the exercise purged her of the passions and evil thoughts she might have had. At a time when Martine and her friends were becoming romantic and reading *On ne badine pas avec l'amour*, Ursula and her comrades were performing marvels at lacrosse and singing, 'I'm so glad . . . I'm not pretty'.

Years may pass, worlds be overturned by wars, governments rise and fall, but the Meltenham rule leaves its indelible imprint upon the soul. The woman I married carried the Meltenham mark even into the way she slept. Some time after she had entered the school, a mistress going the rounds of the icy dormitories one winter's night discovered Ursula sleeping rolled up in a ball under the sheets.

'My child,' she said, 'is that a decent position to sleep in? Just suppose you were to die in the night, would that be the suitable deportment for meeting your Maker?'

From that night Ursula slept according to rule: on her back with her feet out in the cold, and her hands crossed upon her breast.

I admit that's a very suitable attitude for the kings and queens immobilized in stone who sleep in Westminster Abbey under the eyes of succeeding generations. But for spending the night with a normally constituted man, there are more convenient attitudes. I should be suppressing the truth if I omitted to say that on my invitation Ursula did try to cultivate a more conjugal slumber, and go to sleep in my arms. But every time the Meltenham rule returned at night to haunt her subconscious. And if I happened to wake, I found myself alongside a statue.

I know. . . . Not all Englishwomen sleep like that. Not every daughter of Albion has large feet and gigantic jaws. There are ravishing Englishwomen, and when they are pretty they make up for all those who are not. There are volcanic Englishwomen, and when the flames get going they flare up for all Great Britain and all her dominions. Ursula was doubtless a 'case'. In the Ursula 'case' love simply wasn't interesting. The storm which broke on the banks of the Wreak had passed over for ever. Shy girls may have overwhelming attacks of boldness, and then withdraw for ever into their true characters.

Sport in general, and competitive sport in particular, never predisposed anyone to the languors of love. The Meltenham mistresses knew that, and by the intensive practice of lacrosse provided an outlet for harmful ideas. When Ursula grew up, riding took the place of lacrosse. There, again, she was unlike those rare phenomena in the jumping world whose activities in no way damp their ardour; the horse broke Ursula. I might perhaps have hoped at the beginning, seeing her abandon her favourite sport, that the calm would reawaken instincts which had grown rusty for want of use. I was wrong: Meltenham prevailed. I soon realized the meaning of the pause and what was expected of me. If she had for the moment given up riding, it wasn't for the sake of a husband, it was for England and the human race. Meltenham and her mother had prepared her for marriage in an entirely Victorian spirit. The day before she left home, Lady Plunkwell had delivered her final advice:

'I know, my dear. . . . It's disgusting. . . . But do as I did with Edward: *just close your eyes and think of England.*' Like her mother and her mother's mother before her, Ursula closed her eyes. She thought of the future of England. And the future of England is certainly something sacred which her children are right to care about, but somehow as far as my poor means were concerned this future was not assured. Doubtless it was decreed that the future of Great Britain would be better assured by me in France. . . .

As soon as Ursula realized that Heaven was not going to grant us its favours she returned to her training. Indeed, she took it up again with an ardour that bordered on frenzy. Rising at six, she spent the whole day with horses, stable boys, the *oxer*, and the Irish hurdle, on the special track I had been foolish enough to have made for her as a wedding present. In the evening, tired out, she supervised the grooming and inspected the harness. When she came in she would take off her boots, throw herself on to a sofa or her bed and sink into sleep, or else take up her cross-stitch (a fox-hunt which never got finished).

She did not refuse to do what she believed to be her duty. But at the decisive moment she always gave me a guilt complex— the feeling of guilt a schoolboy has when he is caught reading the Medical Dictionary.

'*You should be ashamed of yourself! . . . Put out the light . . . Naughty boy!*'

Was there a fire smouldering somewhere under this ice floe? I am cautious about women in general, and particularly about English women. Under a mask of coldness inadmissible yearnings may be seething. One Sunday I found Ursula reading the *News of the World*, and enjoying the carefully prepared report of one of those conjugal dramas which are the Sunday joy of even the steadiest of English homes. It was the story of an honest Liverpool tradesman who was seeking his freedom after ten years of slavery, during which his wife forced him to play at horses and drove him round the room with a whip. Ursula burst into sarcastic laughter:

'That would suit you perfectly!'

I don't know if it would have suited me, but the idea of a Major in the Indian Army harnessed like a pony and shaking the bells of his harness made a somewhat startling picture. I began to wonder whether Ursula's indifference was only apparent, and whether that habit of going on with her damned cross-stitch right up to the psychological moment was not, after all, the mark of a pervert.

Decades of light years lay between me and Martine's planet, the emotional universe of the French. May I now pass on from the particular to the general and, after carefully emphasizing that England is not exclusively peopled with Ursulas, note down what I consider an essential difference between the two countries? The English observe rites for making tea, and have habits in making love. The French devote to love the care we bring to making tea. In general, love with us is a kind of rapid sketch, to be discussed neither beforehand nor afterwards. For the French it is a full-length, most carefully produced play, arranged with a prologue and intervals, and much discussed before, during and after. The French are the gastronomes of love, the English its executants.

Far from asking, like Martine: 'Was it nice? Are you pleased? Very, very pleased?' Ursula would sooner have asked me if I felt better. In point of fact she didn't ask me anything. This behaviour, moreover, is not peculiar to Ursula; far from it. Even when they like love, the English don't talk about it. They leave that to their dramatists or newspapers.[1] Probably the loveliest love-duets in any tongue were written by Shakespeare. But his isn't the language the English use for current consumption. And

---

[1] Who have their own way of speaking of it. *The New Statesman and Nation* of 27th March 1954 quotes this sentence from an article in the *News of the World*— 'Love is a word we have got to be very careful about. In certain connections it has a sexual significance'.

if they happen to talk of love (as the French, who like to talk of and make love) they adjust their national tongue and add a little local colour to their vocabulary with imported terms like *C'est l'amour* or *Rendezvous*.[1]

As for the Press, it doesn't hesitate, as we have seen, to report conjugal dramas or to embroider endlessly a princely idyll, provided it is princely. Let a Royal Princess change her cavalier or lose her smile before setting out for Southern Rhodesia and all the newspapers with the largest circulation set about finding reasons for her depression. '*Why is the Princess so sad?*' and then my England, my strict soft-hearted England, so tightly laced in the corset of its traditions, always ready to be moved by a romance, all that England which feels it really owns the Royal Family, becomes passionately anxious to discover whose face it is that is floating through the Princess's imagination while she contemplates the dances of the feathered warriors of Bechuanaland. Very respectfully, but with an insistence which would be out of place in a less polite country, reporters scrutinize the sad countenance, trying to find out what is behind it. Then their austere governess, *Miss Times*, calls them to order in fifteen lines.

I have always tried to measure as accurately as possible and in every detail the distance which separates Frenchmen from Englishmen. I wish I could do this with their sentimental affairs, but my dividers fall from my hands. The barrier isn't a moat, it is an abyss.

In France a pretty woman (every woman manages to be pretty in this country, even those that aren't) would be shocked if a man didn't pay her some attention in a drawing-room, or didn't even notice her new frock. She might possibly conceive of such an attitude in a husband, while publicly deploring that he no longer sees her with a lover's eyes.

In England a pretty woman finds it 'most shocking' if a man kisses her hand, and very bad form if he compliments her on her

[1] Quoted in French. It is interesting to note that an up-to-date French girl who finds '*Je vous aime*' old-fashioned will cheerfully write, '*I love you*'.

complexion, unless of course he is her husband and then he wouldn't think of doing it.

What Martine asks of a dress is that it should be elegant. Ursula and her friends wanted something *to be comfortable in*.[1] Out of doors the Parisian wearing a new spring tailor-made is secretly delighted to see the glint it produces in a man's eye. So would an Englishwoman be of course, but such a spark is hard to imagine in a land where a man's glance, probably because of the surrounding dampness, seems to be uninflammable. Frenchmen gaze at women: Englishmen pass them by.

In France women do all they can to be noticed, while expressing great surprise if a man they don't know notices them enough to say so. A *femme du monde*[2] is scandalized if she is accosted, but bitterly disappointed if she isn't. 'I'm never followed now', she will say one day, thereby acknowledging her age and her disillusionment.

An Englishwoman can be perfectly confident on this matter: nobody will accost her. If such an extraordinary thing should happen, and some suspicious-looking foreigner thought of following her, the traditional policeman would soon restore things to their traditional order. The policemen of the two countries in this, as in other things, are very different. Martine once told me that when she was very young, but not too young to be followed, she rushed up to a policeman and said: 'Monsieur l'agent, that man is following me!' 'Sorry I can't do the same, Mademoiselle!' said the policeman, calmly continuing to direct the traffic. These are only minor differences.[3]

The real antagonism lies elsewhere. Often when a Frenchman is being spoken of you are told a little about himself, a lot about his mistress, and nothing at all about his wife. When an Englishman is being discussed you are told a lot about him, but very little

---

[1] I must confess that in dress Englishwomen have made marked progress in the last few years. But acquired habits stick. (*Major's note.*)

[2] In France a *femme du monde* means a woman who doesn't belong to anybody (not even to her husband), probably in contradistinction to the *demi-mondaines* who belong to everybody. (*Major's note.*)

[3] It should be noted that if the methods of the police in Paris and London vary, their effect on 'followers' is the same; the man makes off.

is said about his wife, and nothing at all about his mistress. I am inclined to believe that a Frenchman without a mistress is like an Englishman without a club, but . . . far be it from me to generalize. I am thinking only of certain town circles, though country girls often conceal under a timid exterior much more boldness than their rivals in the cities.

One thing is clear: the result of Frenchmen's predilection for a love affair, and the care they take in bringing up their children in the respect of family traditions, is that of all countries in the world France is the one in which it is simplest to live a complicated life and most complicated to live a simple life. With us the complications are rather less visible. Being without children lessens hesitations about divorce. On the other hand we hesitate longer before committing a *crime passionnel*.

An Englishman is governed by the 'it isn't cricket' law even in his sentimental embarrassments (and there's never anything comic about that even on the stage): he has to know how to part with his wife as gracefully as he would lose a game. If, 'unfortunately', he should show himself a bad loser and kill his rival, he is soon told that this is one of the things that isn't done. He need not count on any indulgence in court. On the other side of the Channel he would doubtless have been congratulated by the jury. At home he receives a polite letter beginning 'Dear Sir' and ending 'Yours faithfully', which tells him that unfortunately and regrettably he will have to be hanged.

In France, where women have legally no rights, everything is done for women by women. The *Rue de la Paix*, magistracy, irony, politics, gallantry, the Republic—all are feminine gender.

In England where legally women have every right, nothing is specially arranged for women, not even men. Ships are feminine, but apart from that the masculine prevails: the greatest compliment one can pay a woman is to say that she is a good sport.[1]

That is just what they said about Ursula. We have seen how Meltenham had developed and masculinized her. In England

[1] A good loyal friend.

everything works in favour of this vast conspiracy against women: the intensive practice of sport during adolescence deprives the female [1] of her tender feelings, the clubs take away her husband, schools take away her children, ready-made clothes obscure her charms and, finally, these very charms fade.

But the age of defeat is her moment of victory. At a time when a Frenchwoman fades into a blur of greys and beiges, the Englishwoman, freed from all constraint, gaily takes her revenge on men. School uniform had suppressed her springtime, so she lives it gloriously later in life, wearing a market-garden on her head, and dolled up in baby-blue or salmon-pink dresses. Then, having proclaimed her equal rights, she acts like a man, frequents her club like a man, goes into politics like a man, and, true woman that she is, becomes President of the Society for Lost Finches.

That honour was not to come to Ursula, but a still more glorious one was in store for her.

She fell at Bombay in the Viceroy's Cup, when the hurdle had been put up to six feet. She had insisted on riding a hard-mouthed Australian stallion.

After refusing the *oxer* Bahadur Sahib hit the wall with his chest and, far from clearing it, came a fatal cropper.

[1] Though much less used than the word 'woman', the term *female* in English has no derogatory implication.

It may seem strange to bring in animals when we are talking of women and love. But England is far less the land of *I love you* than the land of *love me, love my dog*.

The French eat horses and all kinds of other animals, but never miss a chance of calling one another *my little cat* or my *little sugar hen*.

The English, on the other hand, who are far more reserved about this form of address and approve of corporal punishment for their children, let themselves go in a welter of tender feelings for ponies or dogs. If a watchman at the Tower happens to break his leg by stumbling over his pike, no one takes any notice. But if Judy, a fox-terrier belonging to one of the yeomen, should fall ill, as happened recently in London, all London is moved to tears by the bulletins the newspapers publish about its health. I don't know if l'Abbé Pierre would have collected as much money over here as he did in France, but I am certain he would have collected much more if he had been campaigning for a home for stray cats. No beggar in the kingdom will contradict me when I say that a professional blind beggar will double his receipts if he is accompanied by a sad-eyed dog. Should his dog become blind, he can begin to think of retiring. (*Major's note.*)

It was a complete tragedy; while the unconscious Ursula was being borne away to the British Hospital, Bahadur Sahib had to be shot.

These two faithful servants of equestrianism now repose in Indian soil.

THE DEAR HEREDITARY ENEMY

THE only drama in my life since the death of Ursula is my son.

First of all his Christian name. I wanted to call him Marmaduke. Since 1066 it has been a tradition with the Thompsons—who through their great-great-grandfather can, with a little pressure on the last branch, manage to link up with William the Conqueror—to call their eldest son Marmaduke. Ursula would not have objected. But my son eventually came to me through my second wife, who is French, and my suggestion made Martine burst out laughing. The name Marmaduke always made her laugh. She says it sounds like Dundee marmalade. . . . *Je ne sais pas, moi . . . pas sérieux.*

What to my mind is not at all 'serious' for an ex-Major in the Indian Army is the name 'Doukie' [1] which she made out of it. Like the good Frenchwoman she is, she can make a dress out of nothing and a pet name out of anything.

We reached a compromise; the child should be called by the first three letters of both our names and we added a c which he could do what he liked with later on. So he is called Marc. But no power in the world will stop me calling him Marmaduke to myself.

Our discussion was merely the prelude to a tragedy which gathered in crescendo with the problem of his education.

Good God! Is it really possible that peoples should have set up as near to one another as we have just for the pleasure of doing everything the other way round?

It is the same with children as with driving a car, or the judicial system: at twenty miles' distance everything is the contrary of everything. The French bring children into the world to watch them grow up. Scarcely have the English seen them born than

[1] Or on very good days Doukie-doukie. (*Major's note.*)

they send them away to grow up elsewhere. North of Boulogne children are brought up among grown-ups. South of Folkestone they become grown-ups among children. In France they are sentimental about them; in England they toughen them. French parents are somewhat annoyed if their sons show no signs of precocious intelligence. The English are dismayed if they show any such signs.[1]

How in such circumstances can we find some common ground?

I thought for a moment that I had found it in the person of Miss ffyfth.[2]

The boy should be brought up at first in France with an English governess. At this threat of invasion all Martine's Breton ancestry raised the alarm: she hesitated a long time over the intrusion of an artificial though consanguineous step-mother. I was supported by some of her friends who admitted: 'Nothing like an Englishwoman for bringing up children', and discouraged by others who said: 'Yes, all very well . . . but you won't see anything of him!'

In the end Martine agreed.

It would be inaccurate to write: 'Enter Miss ffyfth.' An icy blast from the North Sea rushed up and down the whole house. With her angular purplish face, her prominent tombstone teeth, her long arms, her bony hands with their scaly skin, Miss ffyfth was the picture of rigidity, the incarnation of the hereditary enemy, Queen Elizabeth condemning Mary Queen of Scots to death, Queen Victoria reclaiming the quagmires of vice with puritanism, Britannia in a golden helmet seated on a barrel of slaves. This lodger from the first country on the left above France installed herself as a *squatter* in our home. It was not exactly war, but the alert had been sounded. In the twinkling of an eye the situation became tense; Florine the cook was not going

---

[1] I don't mean to say that my honourable compratriots adore idiotic children. But they like children to be children. In France what they like best in a boy is the hint of the man he is going to be. An English father likes to tell you something his son said if it has a comically childish character. Unlike the Frenchman, he won't be proud if the child said something forward for his age. (*Major's note.*)

[2] Without a capital. See further on. (*Major's note.*)

to make porridge for that dragon (*ça n'y avait rien à faire*), nothing doing, and Clarissa told her to her face she could starve before she got meals in her room.

I had known Miss ffyfth in India. After doing her first service in some of the swellest nurseries in the kingdom, Miss ffyfth had been summoned to Kashmir by an Anglomaniac rajah who had decided to entrust to her the training of his indolent, dreamy and rather round-shouldered son. Miss ffyfth forced this oriental youngster to wear a rod across his shoulder blades and trained him with long hygienic walks ('Breathe deeply . . . head up . . . one two, one two') to march like one of Her Majesty's Grenadier Guards, fists swinging violently backwards and forwards. Finally, she produced a quite creditable being. When the Englishwoman left Srinagar the boy was still an Indian, but he was straightened up; he no longer dreamed of comparing a young girl's eyes to hibiscus flowers; his indolence was discarded and he admitted that Siva had tried to perfect the monsoon in an unsuccessful attempt to test British waterproofs.

At first there were terrible battles over pronunciation. It is difficult for a child who is not completely English to admit that Beauchamp is pronounced 'Beecham' and Leicester 'Lest'r'. But nobody in the house from the boy upwards ever managed to pronounce Miss ffyfth's name correctly. It's a difficult name to whistle, even for the British. Now Miss ffyfth, who claims that she could give a course of private lessons on her name alone, is very much attached to her patronymic.

Very rare are those families who from medieval times have retained the privilege of beginning their names with a double ration of small f's.[1] Rarer still are those who can add the luxury

[1] The Major is alluding to those ffoulkes, ffordes, ffrangcon-Davies and other french (no capital) old families who feel singularly *f*fortified by this impregnable rampart, and guard their privilege very jealously. In this respect Miss ffyfth's case is very significant; if she never married it was from a desire to keep her name rather than her person intact. When she was twenty she fell in love with Merthylyd llynfartha. None of the daughters in her family had ever married a man whose name didn't begin with ff or Ff. Her father, after rapidly proving that two ll's make no difference, ordered her to stop that nonsense. And so Miss ffyfth remained a virgin. (*Major's note.*)

of a 'th'. Only a thousand years' practice can bring off this tricky recovery of the tongue without a slip. The French stumble over it and that irritates them. Old Florine remarked that she did not need such an expenditure of f's, she would manage just as well with one. '*Le jour où elle ff . . . ra le camp, l'Anglaise, elle peut s'en coller quatre des f . . . ça ira plus vite!*'

Martine, who was beginning to lose her self-control, tried to get her own back by serving up some Broglie, Maupéou, and even some la Trémouille, but the warlike Welsh jaw swallowed the old French nobility whole; that showed the hereditary enemy.

The tension increased. Martine began to realize that some of her friends had been right. After seven o'clock she couldn't see her son without having a scene. Rules must be respected. Miss ffyfth meant to dress the child, put him to bed, and get him up, as *she* wished it done, otherwise she refused all responsibility. British rule!

Martine agreed to be patient a little longer, but it embittered her character. Her mind became strangely retrospective. Hitherto she had never seemed to know who came first, the Normans or the Saxons. Suddenly she strode through the dense forest of English dynasties and hurled at my head that Gourdon who was flayed alive by Richard Cœur de Lion, as if she had just finished a thesis on the Plantagenets. At those moments she detested me. I couldn't understand, she suggested, because I was English, before all things, English.

I don't take offence for so little. When a Frenchman begins by telling me: 'I will be frank with you, in my family we have always detested the English . . .' I would wager a bottle of Scotch that he will soon assure me, 'But really we're very fond of you. . . .' For a Frenchman there are always two men in every Englishman, a good one (the Oxford *v.* Cambridge one) and the bad one (the Fashoda one). It depends upon his temper.[1] Everyone knows that the really authentic enemy of France is Germany, but faithful as they are to their old supplier of acri-

---

[1] The Frenchman's temper. (*Enemy's note.*)

mony (who might otherwise find himself unemployed) many Frenchmen continue to hand down from father to son the idea of the hereditary British enemy, the most steadfast and cordial antagonist of the Frenchman in time of peace.

To be just, it must be admitted that Miss ffyfth had rather a special way of teaching children History. Sometimes from upstairs I could hear her venturing into the Hundred Years War. 'Then King Edward III, led by one of YOUR peasants, Gobin Agache, crossed the River Somme, and arrived at a village called Crécy, where he made up his mind to wait and see. . . .'

And the King of England did wait. And he saw the French knights coming. And then began the story which was to last a hundred years of those mobile English archers armed with wooden bows made of supple ash, their quivers on their hips, always fresh and nimble, and of the French knights entangled in their armour, who charged in vain under a hail of arrows and never had any luck with the rain. *Too bad for the French. . . .* But, added Miss ffyfth, they were *badly led*; they were stifled under their steel helmets, and their methods of warfare were (even then) *old-fashioned. . . .*

Often in winter after sunset I still think about the Hundred Years War and about those names—Crécy, Poitiers, Agincourt, which echo in a school in Dorsetshire like shouts of triumph, while twenty leagues away in a Normandy lycée they sound the knell of French chivalry. Then, as twilight falls and fifty proud little English schoolboys feel the blood of the Black Prince coursing through their veins, sadness fills the hearts of fifty proud little French schoolboys who see John the Good (but Imprudent) led away into captivity in England. Too bad really. . . .

Meanwhile, Miss ffyfth was marching on apace into History. She was sorry for Joan of Arc who was burnt for a witch, but she was careful to point out that the tribunal which condemned her was composed of Frenchmen, and that King Charles VII did nothing to aid the girl (stupendous!). Soon she would get to Napoleon. Without even speaking of Trafalgar or Waterloo,

Wellington had already beaten Napoleon at Vimieiro, remember, and finally the tiresome little man with his funny little black hat had never been able to realize his dream and go to England. For there was ... the sea ... *la mer* ... and, above all, the Br ... the Brr ... the British navy, dear. ...

Napoleon could only see England from afar for a few minutes on board the *Bellerophon* which was taking him to St Helena, but ...

'But he was not permitted to land. ...'

Not everyone is permitted to land, you see. Napoleon, however Napoleonic he might be, had to obey the British rule. Marc was probably unconvinced. Miss ffyfth was surprised by his melancholy. ... She could not understand that a terrible global war was raging in the poor child's brain: that there was in him a little of Wellington and a little of Napoleon (with a slight prejudice in favour of the man with the funny hat—so attractive in spite of everything) and that in the French half of his mind Grouchy arrived on time at the Battle of Waterloo, while Miss ffyfth had already got Napoleon on St Helena.

Miss ffyfth's reign lasted two months. It came to an end with the third cook and sixth housemaid she had driven crazy with her unreasonable demands and her early morning tea.

One day, realizing there was something ineradicable in the French character (perhaps an anti-Miss), she departed with great dignity, having tried to *do her duty to make a real man of Marc*. But the withering look she gave me when I had been forced to surrender (it was a choice between cooks and her)—oh ... Miss ffyfth, that damned look will haunt me even in the grave.

The 1939 war was to consolidate Miss ffyfth's territorial conquests in the tender domain of Marc. Our son was on holiday in England when the conflict broke out: we decided he should pursue his studies at a school in Shropshire.

When Marc came back to France he was completely transformed; with his cap, his grey flannel trousers and navy blue waterproof, he seemed definitely British. He had been taught that the earth is a planet on which you find England and a large

MISS FFYFTH GIVES NOTICE

heap of sand, the Sahara, which was left to the French so that they could amuse themselves with a railway they were always talking of making. He knew that the most enviable of all possible arrangements that one could ever dream of is incontestably the geographical situation of Great Britain which shelters it from want and from the tiresome promiscuity of foreign invasion. He had admitted that the French, though they might be versatile, agricultural and witty, had never been able to build really good ships, though they did what they could to become gentlemen by just once in their lives buying a hat at Lock's. Brought up under the hard law of masters ever ready to manipulate the supple cane, and of prefects quick to strike, he had recognized that the making of a gentleman begins by accepting a licking without grumbling.

Martine was surprised to find that he seemed to have an instinctive aversion for hand-kissing, and horrified when she discovered that he said, 'Good night, Mummy', without kissing her.

A week later Marc entered a French school. There he learnt that Joan of Arc had heard real voices (not just 'voices'), that a bold seaman named Suffren had had to go right to the Bay of Bengal to find the English ships to teach them a lesson, and that in exchange for Canada and India which had escaped from French hands (*tout à la Pompadour*) England had given only very small change, a few of the lesser Antilles, together with the 5 (five) trading stations: Pondicherry, Chandernagor and the three others whose names one never remembers. Good as they were at cricket and golf, the English had nothing really comparable to the *Querelle des Anciens et des Modernes*. Finally, it was always the French who bore the first brunt in warfare, because the English took so long to dress up as soldiers.

Nine months later, exhausted by the word-for-word translation of the *De Senectute*, and the vain pursuit of the square on the hypotenuse, the poor child was nothing but a living chaos. Flung from Trafalgar Square to the Place d'Iéna, and from Waterloo Station to the Gare d'Austerlitz, he discovered that in the end men fight only for railways or cross-roads, and that the Latins in particular spend their lives in the streets named after the 29th July, or 4th September, without exactly knowing what really happened on those days.

In all this incoherence our son seemed to feel quite lost. At all costs something had to be done to save his tottering reason.

'In any case,' said Martine, 'there can be no question of sending him back to one of your beastly English schools!'

'Nor will I,' I retorted, 'let him grow round-shouldered in one of your damned French lycées!'

In the end we sent him to Switzerland, that marvellous little country which always manages to get the best out of every war, domestic or external.

FRENCH AS SHE IS SPOKE

I HAVE long tried to discover, without asking point blank, how to speak good French.

In pocket guides you will find: *Excusez moi ... Y'-a-t-il quelq'un ici qui parle anglais? ... Je suis étranger* written, to make it easier for you: *Ekskyze-mwa ... i jatil kelkoe isi ki parle aglé? ... ze suiz étrazé. ...*

One such book has enriched my vocabulary with a host of expressions like: *Garçon, le jacquet (le zake)* or *Perçoit-on un droit de péage pour traverser ce pont? ...* (Do I have to pay toll to cross this bridge?). Its usefulness in case of need I do not deny, but I am ready to part with it at a reasonable price to any real amateur of language.

My difficulty with these handbooks—full of *tireboutons* (tirbuto) and *harengs bouffis* (bufi) [1] so difficult to bring in at the right moment—for a time compelled me to attempt to follow the example of my honourable countrymen and adopt the lazy solution of not trying to speak French or else speaking it so badly that the French who pride themselves on 'spiking English' come to your aid and air some of the English they learnt at the lycée: *ze dineur iz raidi.* This ensures, then, not only that you will not be understood but that you will not understand anybody else.

For a British subject there is a third method: not to attack the French language directly, but to try and bring your vocabulary up to date by taking advantage of such sojourns in Canada or Belgium as war or government missions may have permitted you to make. But I must warn you of the dangers of such a system.

I had put my trust in the Canadians, who assure us that they

---

[1] Readers who might think that the Major is exaggerating may like to refer to the source of his information: if it amuses them they will find *un jacquet* on p. 81 of the *Mémento anglo-français* by William Savage (with key to pronunciation and appendices). As for the *harengs bouffis* (bloaters) they may be found swimming about on p. 147 of the *Travellers' Foreign Phrase Book* by J. O. Ketteridge, F.S.A.A.

are the only people in the world who speak pure French: the
French of Montaigne. Yet I would not advise any of my compatriots to ask in a shoe shop for a pair of 'claques' if he wants
snow-boots, nor to ask a commissionaire for a 'char' if he wants a
taxi.

The Belgian experiment, if, as in my case, it precedes the stay
in France, is even more dangerous. I remember the cunning
expression of the house agent when I arrived in Paris from
Liège, and asked if he could find me a flat 'à quatre places'.[1]
'Facing the engine?' he inquired, and his smile showed me that
I was now in the land of repartee, and perhaps about to be
'certified'.

No doubt about it, to speak really good French you must learn
it in France. Surely the least I could do after marrying a Frenchwoman was to share her words. But once on the spot things
became even more complicated. I knew already that north of
the Ardennes there was one way of speaking French and another
way south of them. I soon realized that there's one way of
speaking French north of the Somme and another south of the
Loire, a third east of the Massif Central, and (roughly) fifty-five
other ways, so that in the end it is impossible to say exactly
who in France speaks French. The citizens of Lyons make fun
of those of Marseilles, those of Bordeaux mock those of Lille or it
may be of the Landes, the inhabitants of Nice mock those of
Toulouse, Parisians mock provincials and all provincials make
fun of the Parisians.

Determined to perfect my French, I set out on a long journey
through France.

Experts had assured me that Touraine was the domain of the
language in its perfection, so I decided to take a Touraine cure.
When I returned to Paris my very British complexion (red
marbled with blue veins) was distinctly heightened in colour
thanks to the Vouvray I had drunk, but when at my first dinner
party I ventured to say of the bourgueil that it was very *gouleyant*
meaning that it slipped smoothly down your throat, they looked

[1] The Belgians say *places* where the French say *pièces* (rooms).

at me as if I were a Yahoo. Later in the evening when, under the fluence of the aforesaid bourgueil, I felt emboldened to tell Martine that she was as *ameugnounante*[1] as one could wish (which, for an ex-Major in the Indian Army, was simply heroic) all I got in the way of thanks was her inquiry, 'Aren't you feeling well?'

Still resolved to try everything to make my French perfect, I continued my travels. Following up a certain sense of logical reasoning, I first went to visit the Tiberghiens at Roubaix whom I had got to know during the war.

M. Tiberghien received me and said, not, 'Asseyez vous' (take a seat) but 'Mettez-vous'.

At first I thought he meant to ask me if I had put on woollen pants, but he merely repeated, 'Mettez-vous', pointing to a chair. So I put myself in it.

A little later when I reached Marseilles I heard M. Pappalardo exclaim as he saw me, 'Remettez-vous, dear Madjor Tomme-pessonne'. I thought he was about to bring me a restorative, but it was merely his way of inviting me to take a seat. So I re-put myself.

The French language varies with the longitude. Still, the point is that most French understand each other more or less. But when a Basque sets about speaking the language of his corner of the earth (and he seems to take a peculiar pleasure in so doing in the presence of a Parisian or a foreigner) then, indeed, you are in an impenetrable fog. After a brief stay in Bordeaux, where I learnt that my laundry had gone to the *lisseuse* to be ironed, I was glad to get back to Paris; I felt more comfortable with Martine.

Do the Parisians know how to speak French or do they not? When at the Daninoses' I hear their little boy say to his sister, 'T'es pas cap de faire ça' or whisper, looking at me (they must think I am more than a bit hard of hearing): 'Did you notice his moustache? Funny sort of fur! And his imper? . . . Impecc! . . .'[2] It's difficult for me to believe that this is the language of Montesq (sorry, Montesquieu).

[1] An Angevin word (formed on 'mignon') meaning attractive.
[2] 'Imper' short for imperméable (mackintosh), 'impec' short for impeccable (wizard).

At this rate, one may even wonder whether in fifty years' time France will not have lost half her vocabulary. You must admit that that would be 'formid' but they are 'cap' of doing it.

To come back to adult Parisians, they would be almost comprehensible to the British if many of them didn't feel obliged to garnish their sentences with truffles of Anglo-Saxon expressions which may be all right for the French, but are all wrong for the British.[1]

The other evening in a drawing-room I heard a good lady, whose words seemed to curl out through her cigarette holder, declare to a man who was holding his head in the clouds of smoke: 'I was invited to the *previou* at the *Heïmarquet Ciateur* in London. It was auquai (okay). . . . But at the première here on Friday evening the audience was simply lousy. Nothing but 'plouks'.

Plouks? Ploucs? Plouques? Larousse is no help here, but I think I gathered they were persons of no importance. In any case they weren't *des gens bien*.

The smoke-engulfed gentleman was surprised (in his own way):

'Jeannot wasn't there?'

'No, not Jeannot nor Marcel nor Jean. Nobody. It was deadly.'

Who were these Jeannots, Marcels, Jeans I was always hearing about in Paris? An actor, a dramatist, and a poet, all equally famous. Obviously this lady and gentleman knew them very well. Yes, intimately, as did three million other Parisians. It is smart in Paris to call people by their Christian names as soon as they have reached a certain degree of fame.

There, again, the French are the contrary of the British: you

[1] The Major is alluding to expressions like *footing* which to the French means *footing* (walking) but means nothing at all to the English, or *smoking* which to the British means smoking (a cigarette) and not a dinner jacket, to say nothing of the Parisian *English tea rooms* which, like the one near the Porte Maillot, put up: *Five o'clock à quatre heures*. In the same way one might cite the case of many a Frenchman who in England, having asked the way to the water-closet, is surprised to be shown the kitchen, the smoking room or winter garden, before discovering the lavatory. (*Translator's note.*)

can be friends with them for ten years, they'll still call you
Monsieur Thompson, but they readily use the Christian name
for someone they don't know, and never will. We who would
not hesitate to call by their Christian names people we've known
only for a few hours, without thereby becoming familiar, would
hesitate to say 'Larry', when we talk of Sir Laurence Olivier,
unless, of course, we were friends of his.

However, there does exist a terrain in which, without quite
meeting, the smart set of both countries can fight side by side:
that of the *h*. To a superficial observer England appears to be a
united nation. In reality she has been divided for centuries by
the war of the *h*.

One of the principal aspirations of the English élite is the
aspirate *h*. An Englishman will go into training for twenty years
to achieve the correct pronunciation of *Her Highness the Princess
of Hanover*. I have known some who have died without achiev-
ing it. To get their own back, the common people (*gens du
peuple*) avoid sounding h's when they do exist (a nice 'ouse) and
put them in in all sorts of places where they don't (a hangel).

In France where this war is far less virulent, a peculiar sub-
stitution (as with us) goes with it: the *e* becomes *a*.[1] Only a few
days ago I heard an affected girl saying with what she hoped was
an English accent:

'J'ai pris le tha chez la Pocha, c'eta parfa.' Martine was good
enough to translate and tell me that this distinguished person
had taken tea with pleasure (I nearly wrote plàsir) with the
Pochets. '*Parfait*', moreover, is only one of a hundred very
fashionable superlatives favoured by these happy few to express
appreciation of an evening, a film, or a play. The most often
used are *Mhãrvhailleux . . . Dhivin . . . Seûblime*. The quint-
essence of chic seems to be to follow up these qualifications with
the word *what*. A balletomane will say, 'It's divine, what?'—
which is his way of saying, 'You're not going to think otherwise, no?' and also a way of dragging you along in his wake and
rushing you at high speed without waiting not to hear what you
haven't yet said.

[1] Rather pronounced ratha. (*Major's note.*)

By Jove! How the devil can an ex-Major in the Indian Army grasp all these damned fine shades of meaning? In this, as in other things, the French adore a paradox. Speaking of a midge lost in the middle of a Picasso canvas, they will say, '*C'est hénaurme*' (enormous). Yet the other day when the Eiffel Tower was being discussed, I heard a lady say, 'Well, anyhow I think it's a little darling.'

I went the other evening to one of those little theatres where they were giving a play of the kind called 'advanced' because you understand it only a long time afterwards. The dialogue was crammed with this sort of pearl:

'Est-ce un fantassin?'

'Non, c'est un hexagone.'

At each of these pearls my neighbour, who was evidently an initiate, emitted a kind of cluck, or gallinaceous hiccough. I saw her in the interval surrounded by a group of connoisseurs who were spreading themselves in '*extraordinaire*' and '*rhe-mâr-quhâble quoi?*' In this land of Descartes there exists an intelligentsia which can find light only in obscurity. Someone went past, however, some obscure *plouk*, eager for enlightenment, who confessed to having understood nothing.

'But why on earth,' said my neighbour, 'must you absolutely *understand* something? How horribly bourgeois you are!'

Strange land! The workers hurl abuse at the bourgeois. The intellectuals make fun of them. The aristocracy despise them. But those who are readiest to run down the bourgeois and to feel affronted by the mere use of the term applied to themselves, are the bourgeois. And the best of it is that from plumbers to peers, including explorers, journalists and actors, the whole country, engulfed as it is in the universal wave of social security, grows more and more bourgeois every day.

France? A nation of bourgeois who try to prove that they are not by attacking those who are.

WHEN THE FRENCH TRAVEL

I SHALL always remember my visit to the stadium of Delphi. Not so much because of the majesty of the site still imbued with the Pythian mystery, but rather for the remark of a Frenchman on a cruise, who, after running his eyes over it, partly for himself, partly for his Kodak, partly for France, said to his wife:

'Doesn't it remind you, darling, of the Jean Bouin stadium?'

This strange reminiscence recalled to my memory the countless remarks made by French people all over the world: those French people who find the Passage du Havre at Milan, the Côte d'Azur in Florida or Vézelay at St James of Compostella. When an Englishman contemplates the Bay of Rio, or St Peter's in Rome, he just thinks about St Peter's or Rio Bay. Not having such a simple mind, a Frenchman will profit by the occasion to evoke the Bay of Naples, or Chartres Cathedral.

When the English set off on their travels they take with them a sponge bag, an umbrella and even (if they are going to France) a little spirit stove for making tea. Yet a Customs official examining their brains would find nothing to declare. M. Taupin may sometimes forget his tooth-brush, but he is always armed with a voluminous case of comparisons against which, so far, all Customs officials have been powerless.[1]

Some time ago I visited Bruges with the Taupins. 'It's extraordinary,' said M. Taupin, 'how much all this reminds me of Venice!'

Six months later in Venice our gondola, after passing the Bridge of Sighs, was making for the Fenice theatre. 'Oh, Tounet,' cried Madame Taupin, 'look over there. Isn't it just like Bruges?'

In these conditions the Taupins, who used to be very stay-at-

[1] The Major believes that in a not too distant future Customs officials will possess a machine for checking up thought.

home, and have only lately been seized with a strong tourist-appetite, normally engage in terrible souvenir-battles. By dint of talking about Bruges in Venice and of Amsterdam in Copenhagen they are now unable to say whether in 1949 they were on the Grand Canal or the Zuyderzee.

In this Realm of Comparison meals occupy an important place: all the more so since the comparison is always made to the advantage of French (the only, *la seule*) cooking. Sure of this supremacy the French are unshakable in their demands. Madame Taupin would herself cheerfully instruct the natives about their specialities. While she is settling down to the *gnocchi alla romana* she explains so fully how she prepares it *à la parisienne* that I don't know whether I am lunching in the plazza Rusticucci or the Place de l'Alma. As for M. Taupin who is worried about his liver, he is always chasing after his cutlet: nothing so difficult to find, he thinks, as plain cooking.

'Ah,' he says, as if he were speaking of some dear dead friend, 'the good old hot-pot.'

A Frenchman's nostalgic longing for his home cooking when he is abroad has always struck me. Is it because the English do not know what it is to suffer from this melancholy that they are able to colonize the whole world and set up house anywhere without any regrets? Perhaps. . . .

If he is a comparison machine for the sights and food of other countries, in hotels and ships the Frenchman becomes a calculating machine. Mme Taupin has a way of using her husband as a currency-conversion apparatus which leaves me speechless. I treasure the memory of an afternoon specially devoted to footwear in the streets of San Sebastian.

'Two hundred and ninety-five pesetas, darling, what does that make?'

Darling explains that you must multiply by nine or by ten according to the rate of exchange:

'About three thousand francs. . . .'

'When I think,' muses Mme Taupin, 'that the same thing in Paris would cost twice as much . . . at least!'

'OH, TOUNET, LOOK OVER THERE. ISN'T IT JUST LIKE BRUGES?'

They went in. And bought. Then met some other French people who had found the same thing at half the price (in the south). The strange thing is that the more the article pleased Mme Taupin the more favourable became the rate of exchange (carefully adjusted by her). With a certain pair of slippers I witnessed the fall of the peseta to 7.50, an unhoped-for affair that summer. On the other hand, M. Taupin was not so fortunate at Bilbao over a trench-coat which suited him but not Madame: that made the peseta suddenly soar to twelve francs.

'I don't want to stop you, Tounet, but really it's ridiculous . . . you'll find the same thing in Paris, only better and not so dear. . . .'

Having compared basilica with cathedrals, volcanoes with countries, rios with canals, pesetas with francs, the Frenchman then discovers fresh resources of comparison between himself and the aborigines. He looks at the world with an amused, often indulgent and readily critical eye, inclined to be the more mocking in proportion as the currency of the country is less steady. To tell the truth, no one seems to him very responsible: the Americans are grown-up children, the English golfers, the Italians spaghetti eaters, the Spaniards toreadors, the South Americans perpetual summer holiday makers. In his heart he is always asking, '*Comment peut-on être Persan?*'

The Englishman doesn't ask himself the same question, at least not in the same way. He has learnt once and for all that the world comprises Englishmen and various other tribes. In a universe which is becoming more and more mixed up, where you find Frenchmen in the Cocos Islands and Kanaks in Stockholm, the Englishman remains an Englishman and doesn't mix with anything. Twenty-one miles of sea and an historical rampart of customs and costumes keep his island free from contamination. He himself, as rarely subject to emotion as to a cold in the head, invariable as his definite article, travels across our planet like a little Great Britain in motion, inaccessible yet near, like his island. He is very much interested in the customs of all these people—so funny, aren't they?—and considers them with the explorative

D

eye of a man who has been sent on a mission to the Zulus, sometimes even venturing to touch them with the tip of his stick or umbrella. Every now and then he is most surprised to discover among these individuals someone who really looks like a gentleman. But instead of wondering how this man comes to be a 'Persian', he muses: 'What a pity it is he isn't British!'

A magic screen brings him an indirect purified vision of the outside world: an invisible waterproof protects him from all external pollution: he emerges intact from the slums of Naples or the hordes of the Brahmaputra. Once he has crossed the frontier, the Frenchman feels obliged to justify his reputation of Don Juan from the capital of two thousand years of seduction. He wants to love and be loved. In his quality of dispenser of the generous principles of 1789, he sets out in search of adventure in the native quarters. The Englishman becomes even more reserved than these reserves, and hurries off to the tea room or to the British Club. At Bombay as at Caracas, in Havana as at Lucerne, everywhere he takes his stand on his cardinal points: bacon, tea, club, whisky. At night with the help of the Almighty he will sleep soundly in an alien land. He knows that at the slightest alarm he can count on his standing as a 'British subject' as in oldest days the Roman did on the prerogative of his status: *civis Britannicus sum*. He is assured of this by his tragic handbook under the heading *Police, complaints*: 'I've had my wallet ... bag ... cloak ... stolen ... Stop thief. Fire! ... Help! ... Drive me to the British Consulate!' One knows that at once the Foreign Office, Scotland Yard and the Intelligence Service will be on their toes. Should the situation worsen and degenerate into a riot, it will be made known that H.M.S. *Revenge*, steaming towards Aden, is bringing protection to Mr Smith.

Perhaps M. Taupin does not feel so sure about his consuls and their powers? While I detest being cluttered up with papers he loves to set out with letters of recommendation. Acquired at the cost of manifold negotiations, these credentials inform the Duke of Rovedrego, the Alcade of Grenada or the Commendatore Ruspolo di Ruspoli that M. Taupin is travelling for his pleasure.

They are all, of course, important people, and since they possess several residences, châteaux or country houses, are always away. Never mind, with all these damned letters which will have no effect upon their addressees, even when they do reach them, M. Taupin feels happier. You never know! [1]

That is how M. Taupin travels. It would be more accurate to say it is how France travels. For what M. Taupin exports with him is the whole of France. An Englishman, convinced as he is of his superiority, contents himself with making it felt (pretty disagreeably at times). The Frenchman is equally convinced of the superiority of his own country; he himself is *La France spirituelle*, gallant France, the France of freedom, Vercingetorix and Christian Dior, Pascal and the Rue de la Paix. He who, at home, seizes on any pretext for disparaging his corporate bodies, who in Paris would rather boost a detective story signed W. A. Thorndyke than one signed J. Dupont,[2] now defends France, her artists, her inventors, with all the fervour of a Crusader. And who would dream of attacking him? Hotel managers, restaurant keepers, drift towards him to inhale a little Parisian air.[3] And M. Taupin receives them on his ambulant territory with good-humoured gratification. The restaurant keeper says, 'Ah, France!' and M. Taupin says, 'Ah! . . .' Then his interlocutor sighs, 'Ah! Paris!' and M. Taupin replies, 'Ah! . . .' And so from Ah! to Ah! the dialogue continues. The whole world melts away, only Paris remains.

'There's nothing like it anyway!' says M. Taupin.

'I lived in the Rua des Chiseaux,' states the Italian.

'Ah,' sighs M. Taupin, 'the good old Rue des Ciseaux!' (He confesses afterwards that it is the first time he ever heard of it.)

'*La Torre di Aiffel!*'

---

[1] It does sometimes happen that one of these people is 'touched' in the postal or effective sense of the word by a letter. He may even occasionally keep his guest for lunch, dinner or between meals, so that M. Taupin, being received as no one is received in Paris, has no time left to see the countryside, which is just too bad. (*Major's note.*)

[2] M. Daninos confided to me that he became known far more quickly as the translator of Major Thompson than when he wrote under his own name. (*Major's note.*)

[3] Abroad every Frenchman comes from Paris. (*Major's note.*)

'Ah! The Eiffel Tower!'

'Les Folies Bergère! . . .'

A touching moment, when after a rather naughtier *ah!*
M. Taupin and the restaurant keeper exchange a sly wink. Then
M. Taupin, generous and chivalrous, concludes with:

'Every man has two countries, his own and then France . . .'

But the foreigner must be on his guard if one day he takes this
saying literally and decides to become naturalized. He may be
reminded pretty quickly that the second country isn't the first,
and if he isn't satisfied . . .

After all, France for the French!

49 MILLION 'SPORTIFS'

THERE are many good moments for visiting France but there is one which might possibly give you a wrong idea: the period from about the 1st to the 25th July. One of my first travels in France took place during that period. I had come from Gibraltar, crossed the Pyrenees and was on my way to Paris, when I was stopped by two gendarmes at a crossroads:

'You can't go through!' they said.

At that time I still retained the English habit of never asking questions, so I complied without asking why. The sight of a grand array of police encouraged me to think that a bandit was about to be rounded up. However, perceiving on the Route Nationale a great crowd conversing gaily with the mounted police, I concluded that the affair must be less dramatic. A column of armoured cars drawn up on the other side, at one of the cross-roads, led me to believe for a moment that there was going to be a march past of the army. Evidently not, because I soon heard the captain of the gendarmes say to a young lieutenant who was showing his impatience by slapping his boot with his cane (his men didn't seem to mind nearly so much):

'Manœuvres or no manœuvres, you stay put!'

It was indeed clear that no one would get through, not the French with their armoured cars, nor Major Thompson with his car, nor even the gentleman who extricated his important person from his important automobile, police pass in hand, and was merely told: 'Do as the rest do. Wait!'—words which I was to hear fairly often during what followed. From all these premises I had deduced that all traffic was held up to leave the way free for the President of the Republic and his suite, when a great cry burst from countless throats:

'There they are! That's them!'

This singular plural led me to suppose for a moment that the

Head of the State was about to appear with my Most Gracious
Sovereigns, who were then in France. Imagine my surprise on
seeing emerge, instead of Gracious Sovereigns, two male individuals, gracelessly swaying on their bicycles, festooned with
inner tubes and tyres and clad in glaring jerseys and exiguous
shorts, covered with mud, altogether rather a shocking sight.
The spectators were kind enough to explain to me—without my
asking—that these fellows were doing a bicycle Tour of France,
and getting to Paris as quickly as possible by the slowest roads,
which seemed to me strange. But, after all, these are things about
which an Englishman, who is never astonished at anything,
should not express any tactless surprise. From time to time in
London a citizen may, from love of sport or to satisfy some
whim, walk down Piccadilly in a red blazer and white shorts, but
it would be the worst of bad taste to turn round and look at him.
Everyone is free to act and dress as he pleases without fear of
being noticed in a country where good taste demands that we
should see people without looking at them.

What amazed me in this instance was not so much the care-
less dress of these gentlemen as the fact that the police brought
all traffic to a standstill for them, and for a line of lorries belonging to suppliers of pâtés and apéritifs which at first sight had
nothing to do with these proceedings, but were—as inquiry
revealed—closely connected with them. I know that there is the
same sort of Tour of England, but how different it is! Our
racing cyclists, far from stopping the traffic, follow it; they stop
at the red lights *comme tout le monde*. They are only amateurs
who, protected by public announcements, apologize for passing
one another, and get off their bicycles to have tea. Above all,
these young men, of whom no one takes any notice, are properly
dressed.[1]

---

[1] The Major is anxious to emphasize in this connection that 'shorts', though
they mean 'courts' in French, are nevertheless long. When a rugby player's
knickers are torn in a scrum, and have to be replaced at once, the player is immediately surrounded by members of his team according to a very carefully prepared
technique, which leaves no chink for indiscreet eyes. With the French, on the
contrary, this technique of surrounding is far more lax and, according to the
Major, constitutes an invitation to see a bit more.

I didn't reach Paris till late that night. I was worried about the situation in Bengal, where—for reasons too long to explain, and, moreover, no one else's concern—I had had to leave Ursula. There were threats of a rising in Calcutta, the police had had to open fire on the mob, and eventually there had been two hundred killed.

I had already heard that much in Gibraltar, but I wanted to know more. So I bought the Late Night, and even the Late Night Special, editions, of an evening paper, where spread across eight columns a heading announced:

GARRALDI ET BIQUET ENSEMBLE DEVANT LES JUGES DE PAIX

Thinking that an important action was drawing to its close, I prepared to read the speeches under the alluring sub-title, *The Florentine demon is betrayed by his servants*, when my eye was attracted to the cross-section map of the Pyrenees which spread across the southern corner of the paper. I learned later that Garraldi and Biquet were the heroes of the Tour de France, and that by juges de paix (magistrates) one should understand, by one of those metaphors so dear to the hearts of French sport-chroniclers, le Tourmalet and l'Aubisque; the 'demon' was the man in the yellow sweater, and the 'servants' the men in his team. As for the two hundred dead in Calcutta, they were buried in four lines under Mount Perdu.

Therefore I can only advise my countrymen if they are desirous of keeping informed about events in the world in general, and in the Commonwealth in particular, not to come to France in July, unless they are prepared to see the Commonwealth submit to the humiliating laws of 'Queen Bicycle'.[1]

---

[1] A passionate debate opened at this moment between the Major and his French collaborator, when the latter recalled that one day when he was passing through London, feeling very worried about the international situation, he had been alarmed by a newspaper heading which summed it up in these terms:

ENGLAND'S DESPERATE POSITION

which to a Frenchman meant '*L'Angleterre dans une situation désesperée*'. An illuminating sub-title: '*In spite of 6-3 be proud of old England*' shed a strange light on the question. The Major's collaborator thought that a grave decision had been

A few days later when I spoke of the Tour de France to my friend Colonel Turlot, confessing that I couldn't understand anything about it, he retaliated by revealing that after having made three attempts to understand something about a cricket match he had had to undergo a lengthy treatment with a psychiatrist. He added:

'Do you know, my dear Thompson, that millions of 'sportifs' daily follow the tour with enthusiasm?'

'Do you mean, my dear Turlot, that they follow the competitors on their bicycles?'

M. Turlot looked at me as if he thought I was joking. No. Certainly the 'sportifs' he spoke of fought every day, but that was merely to buy the Late Extra Special, or to have the best place to see the finish.

I discovered there a fresh and fundamental difference between our two countries. The English call themselves sportsmen when they practise some sport: the French call themselves sportsmen when they look on. So that, painful as the truth may seem to my countrymen, *there are more sportsmen in France than in England*. Moreover, it couldn't be said that the French don't go in for sport because they are only onlookers. At the cinema, for example, especially at the time of the Tour de France, M. Charnelet comes in really to relax. And then after the news, there he is, obliged to climb on his bicycle and to cover 700 kilometres of the route (for though the competitors cover only one stage at

---

taken, when his eye was caught by the little square space reserved for stop press news where he read:

TEST SCORES

ENGLAND: FIRST INNINGS 435. HUTTON 169, COMPTON 64. RAMADIN 6-113, ATKINSON 3-78. FALL OF WICKETS: 1-1, 2-12, 3-16, ETC.

which explained everything.

On making inquiries he learned that the desperate situation was England's in football, when for the first time in ninety years she had been beaten by Hungary (6-3). And the stop press was about cricket.

'How can you,' said the Major, 'compare an historic match which was national humiliation with your damned bicycle race?'

The Major's face having become purple in a symptomatic fashion, as also the blue line of his temples which made up the British flag in the great days, it seemed better to avoid an explosion and close the discussion.

a time, the spectator has to absorb five or six, and, whether he wants to or not, has to climb Mt Galibier or go down the Col d'Albos). M. Charnelet, whose wishes have not been consulted, is obliged to keep on, over the frightful cobblestones of Normandy, he has a puncture in the neighbourhood of Longwy, skids, sets off again, though he has dropped behind, kisses an Alsatian girl on the way, in spite of his boils climbs up the treacherous hairpin bends of Mt Ventoux, and, as a final penalty, crosses the desolate waste land of the Crau.

There is nothing so exhausting as to be forced to cross the Crau in a cinema in the Champs Élysées at about 20.30 hours. The group straggles, the group dawdles, the group re-forms, the group gets mixed up. It is estimated that there are a million Frenchmen who mentally incorporate themselves in this company, and feel for a moment that they have the legs—what did I say?—I mean the golden flexed muscles of Garraldi or the Demon of the Hills, or the relentless calves of Biquet, that plucky little Frenchman whose luck so often deserts him but who can do wonders at the critical moment.

In the stadiums, at the ringside, or around tennis courts, the French have a way of gesticulating, struggling and generally taking exercise, which contrasts pretty strongly with the attitude of a normal Englishman. Take a boxing match in France and England. It looks like the same sport. In reality it is two very different things. England was the cradle of boxing and other sports. Boxing, tennis, football, golf, are all English children. With the passage of time they have become emancipated, they have travelled, they have been made to marry beneath them. The purity of their essence has been polluted. Between those elderly spinsters who, in order to see the Wimbledon finals, spend the night on camp stools discussing Drobny's drop shot or Rosewall's back hand as they would a stitch in knitting, and the young fans round the Roland-Garros courts, who call faults 'carottes' and lobs 'chandelles' (especially if it is a foreigner who does them), there is an almost interstellar difference. No matter! Whatever Colonel Turlot may say, the sport's ancestors are

'MANŒUVRES OR NO MANŒUVRES,

YOU STAY PUT!'

English.[1] The noble art of delivering blows and avoiding them was already honoured under William the Conqueror while the French were still fighting with their feet round the gates of Paris. Today what happens? What we go to see takes place in the ring. In Paris they fight in the *salle*. With us you could hear a pin drop. In France you wouldn't hear a machine-gun. In England gentlemen in dinner jackets gravely discuss the great value of evasive action, and the referee is respected like a god. In France the only thing which is respected is attack, and the referee is argued with, insulted, abused: he is an enemy. Finally, while the French hurl sarcastic taunts at the weaker combatant, the English encourage him.

This respect for the weaker competitor, and the almost instinctive desire to give him a chance, are the unwritten laws of the Realm, and are obeyed in the same way by fishermen and huntsmen. To discredit someone for ever, an Englishman will say of him: 'He's shooting a sitting bird.' I am alarmed by the knowledge that in France this rule that a bird when on the ground must not be shot is—I am told—not always respected, though, of course, I don't believe it.[2]

An Englishman's fishing is directed by this same difficult cult. On parts of the Test, one of the noblest waters in Hampshire, it is considered a crime to fish the 'evening rise'; at the very moment

[1] Colonel Turlot, who was present, now violently attacked the Major. Armed with a Larousse he dealt him many a formidable dictionary blow. 'Cricket,' he read feverishly, 'favourite exercise with the English, is in reality only a modification of the ancient French game of *la crosse*. Is sometimes written in the French fashion, *criquet. . . .*'

'Ridiculous!' cried the Major.

'Golf,' continued the Colonel, with the utmost calm, 'very possibly owes its origin to the old French game *le mail.*'

'Preposterous! Absurd!' sneered the Major.

'Tennis,' continued the Colonel, with imperturbability, 'developed out of the old French game *la longue paume.*'

'Everyone knows that lawn tennis was invented by my ancestor Major Wingfield in 1874,' exploded the Major, getting very red, and to avoid worse happenings he went off to get some tea.

'Tea,' he emphasized, slamming the door.

[2] Rather a hypocritical remark, since the Major is entirely convinced of the contrary.

when the light fades and the trout become 'easier', the gentleman who has spent the day in torrid heat lying in wait for a fish, packs up and goes back to London. Need I add that to use a worm for bait is a dreadful crime, and that the pseudo-sportsmen who use a wet fly are looked at askance?

I do not doubt that French sportsmen are moved by an equal desire for fairness. Yet they are so different. When an Englishman lands the salmon of his life, he has it stuffed. The Frenchman eats it, after being photographed with his catch. If an Englishman catches an undersized trout, he throws it back. A Frenchman would rather eat it. The Frenchman always eats, not because he is hungry, but—apart from that fear of being ridiculous, which haunts us so little and affects him so much, if he comes home empty-handed—because any amusement seems silly to him if it does not serve some purpose.

Such utilitarian preoccupations do not affect us. But it is repugnant to the French to do things which aren't useful. (I have been told that they have three children rather than two, not through carelessness but because of the family allowance.) A father makes his son learn English, not for the beauty of the language (always a relative affair in the eyes of a Frenchman), but because *cela peut lui servir plus tard* [1]—it may be useful later on. In the Turlot family there is always a son who learns German so that he can be an interpreter in time of war.

Unlike the French, the English adore doing things which, strictly speaking, serve no purpose. It is only in affairs of the heart that they hate doing anything superfluous, like paying court, or even making love. But as soon as it's a question of serious enterprises like fishing and shooting, even the most modest of them will ruin himself by expending vast reserves of uselessness for the love [2] of sport.

Much more could be said about the way sport is treated by the

[1] Quoted in French. The Major was annoyed by the doubt expressed in this opinion and refused to translate it.

[2] The French may be indifferent fishermen, yet they are masters in the art of playing their catch when they are courting a woman, and they are unequalled in getting what they want with women by discussing Proust or the cinema. (*Major's note.*)

JULES INTRODUCES THE ENGLISH STYLE OF FISHING

English and ill-treated by the French. I now perceive that after having written a great deal, I have not yet said anything about the sport which the greatest number of Frenchmen enjoy (two million as against two hundred thousand who play bowls). I mean motoring. That in itself calls for special consideration and deserves to be studied in some quiet corner where one can meditate on the subject without any risk of being run over. Perhaps you will have this good fortune or perhaps you can read between the (traffic) lines. . . .

FRANCE AT THE STEERING WHEEL

BEWARE of the French in general but particularly on the French roads. It is essential for an Englishman arriving in France to realize at once that there are two kinds of Frenchmen: those who go on foot, and those who go in cars. The on-foot loathe the in-cars, and the in-cars terrorize the on-foot, though the first pass instantaneously into the camp of the second the moment their hands are on a steering wheel. (It is the same at the theatre with late-comers: after disturbing a dozen people in order to get to their seats, they are the first to protest about those who have the cheek to arrive later.)

The English on the whole drive badly but prudently. The French on the whole drive well but wildly. The proportion of accidents in the two countries is about the same. But I feel more comfortable with people who do good things badly than with those who do bad things well.

The English (and Americans) have long been convinced that a car travels less quickly than an aeroplane.

The French (and most of the Latins) still seem determined to prove the contrary.

In the heart of many a Frenchman there slumbers a Nuvolari ready to be awakened by the mere contact of his foot with the accelerator. The peaceful citizen who kindly invited you into his car can be metamorphosed under your very eyes into a demoniacal driver. Jérôme Charnelet, that kind of family man who wouldn't squash a fly on a window pane, is quite ready to flatten out one pedestrian per mile provided he feels within his rights. At the green light he sees red. Then nothing will stop him, not even the amber one. On the road this man you thought so steady-going steadily refuses to make way for anyone. It is only when he is absolutely obliged to, and after a brisk fire of hooting, that with very ill grace he will consent to leave the middle of the road. (The English keep to the left. Most people keep to the right. The French opt for the middle, which this time is not the *juste milieu*, happy mean.)

The mere fact of being overtaken puts M. Charnelet in a vile temper. He recaptures his serenity only when he overtakes some new rival. Meanwhile, all his family has to do is to behave well. Woe betide Mme Charnelet if, when asked for it, she can't discover in the car the 'Southern Half of France' which he left behind with the map carrier on the drawing-room chimney-piece. Woe betide her if she doesn't instantly answer the question 'Avallon–Châlons, how far?' Even if she does answer, M. Charnelet, five foot eight of sadism once his foot is on the accelerator, is already enjoying the pleasure he will get out of proving that her calculations are wrong. The children, too, are well trained, 'When your father's thirsty you shall have a drink'. Above all, no untimely stops, 'You should have done it before', says M. Charnelet. They suffer in silence in honour of that all-powerful goddess of the average Frenchman: Average Speed.

When an English motorist prepares to do 300 miles in England, he thinks about doing 300 miles.

When a Frenchman gets into his car to do 600 kilometres, two-thirds of his mind is taken up with his average speed, the other third is filled with asterisks and forks. I mean those famous symbols in his beloved Michelin. His dream, after having kept up an average of 90 for three hours, is to find a restaurant ✖✖☺☺☺ if possible in a site ✹✹✹ near a 📟 (trustworthy) to check the sparking plugs and the oil.

The Englishman will just allow himself to think about a ⬭ after drinking some good *t*. That is if he stays in England. If he goes to France he must first of all force himself to drive on the right side of the road, which in his eyes is the wrong side. That is the most delicate problem. The French have a way of keeping to the right, while continually sliding to the left, which strongly recalls their leanings in politics: the staunchest conservatives refuse to be called 'right' at any price. That's why when an English motorist gets to France, he has some difficulty in knowing where to drive. In reality he would have to push on to

Kenya before meeting again with normal people who drive on
the left, calculate in miles, use avoirdupois weights and measures,
and whose normal temperature is 98·4.[1] Meanwhile, he must
accustom himself to that monotonous metric-system zone, which
leaves no room for the glorious uncertainty of our old measures:
ounce, bushel or peck. A kilometre is always stupidly a thousand
metres, whereas with us the mile is marvellously eight furlongs,
a furlong two hundred and twenty yards, a yard three feet, a foot
twelve inches. . . . It is true that the *Perfect Travellers' Pocket-
Book* puts things right by reminding him that to transfer centi-
grade into fahrenheit 'you merely multiply by 9, divide by 5 and
add 32 degrees'. As for converting kilometres into miles it's
even easier: 'Multiply by 5 and divide by 8.'[2]

During one of my first tours in France, when I was suffering
from the combined effects of a bad chill and an even worse crossing, I thought I would stop at an hotel in Calais and take my
temperature. As the thermometer registered only 40·3 I set out
again in all confidence, raising the hood of my car, and was
rolling pleasantly along with the wind screen open when I
remembered I was among those damned Continentals who can
never do anything like anybody else. I immediately applied
myself to converting my continental temperature into fahrenheit,
and kilometres into miles.

I was about to multiply 274 by 5, to divide by 9 and add 32
degrees to the distance between Calais and Paris, when the sight
of another car coming in the opposite direction on the same side
of the road as myself made me suddenly realize that, lost as I was
in my calculations, I had forgotten to drive on the right. I
changed over to the right side and braked in time, while my
vis-à-vis pulling up just short of me assailed me point blank:
'Completely cracked, you old idiot? Think you're still among
the *rosbifs*?'

Then, taking my silence for incomprehension, he let in the

[1] Fahrenheit, of course. (*Major's note.*)
[2] Once again, the Major is not inventing. These practical hints are given in the
Travellers' Foreign Phrase Book by J. O. Ketteridge, f.s.a.a., for the use of the
English, already mentioned, p. 86.

FRENCH MOTORISTS—ALL CERTIFIABLE?

clutch and looked at me, tapping his forehead with his fore-finger.

I was soon to learn that this gesture is a veritable rite.

Many a time since then I have been on the road with M. Taupin or M. Charnelet and have seen them, for reasons which were often obscure, glare at a motorist they were passing tapping their foreheads the while. Very often the one who is overtaken catches up with M. Taupin and for a no less mysterious motive speaks to him in the same dumb language, though this time he uses his first finger like a kind of screwdriver on his temple. I have deduced from this that the French spend their time on the roads asking one another if they aren't mad, and nearly always find someone at once to confirm that they are.

It is curious to note that a large number of people who, armed with the approved dictionary, are ready to do battle for their idea of 'correct' language are apt to lose all verbal restraint and all sense of propriety as soon as they are in a car. The French, who are born grammarians as others are born navigators or musicians, abandon syntax immediately they are at the wheel.[1] M. Taupin, who devours the column of his newspaper devoted to the defence of the French language, and would not hesitate to reprimand a journalist who wrote *partir à*, instead of *partir pour*, then gets through an impressive consumption of *tête de lard* or *peau de fesse*. In the land of moderation it is always surprising to see people losing their self-control. But the fact of losing it with their hands on the wheel may be pregnant with grave consequences. At least one must do them this justice; you hear them coming a long way off. The golden rule for English motorists is to pass unnoticed. The Frenchman's aim is rather to alarm everyone on the road until there is nobody to be seen. To achieve this he makes as much noise as possible. Most of the

[1] It is easy to see, then, why the French were so surprised by the public apology which appeared lately in the agony column of *The Times*, from a repentant motorist to one of his countrymen on whom he launched a rather violent epithet. A Frenchman would rather have sought to catch up with his adversary and say a bit more, or by means of some skilfully executed wobbling make him collide with a plane tree. (*Major's note.*)

world's motor cars run on petrol. French cars drive on their horns. Especially when they are stopped.[1]

One might think that the Frenchman's speed appetite was determined by the horse power of his car. That is an error. The smaller his car the faster he wants to go. In this realm of paradox the least dangerous cars are the most powerful ones: their drivers, having become blasé, are the only ones who enjoy the luxury of driving well within the maximum, and of accelerating without effort.

As for Frenchwomen, one must do them this justice: they do drive more slowly than the men. An Englishman might therefore logically believe he would be safer with them. That's another error. In a country where everyone goes so fast this very slowness constitutes a most terrible danger. Add to that a certain variability in pace, and that charming spirit of indecision from which one may deduce from the left trafficator that the driver-ess is going to turn right (though it isn't quite certain), and you will realize that there is nothing so hazardous as being driven by a woman. . . .

There exists, however, a super-danger in this country where, as in many others, women don't know how to smoke or drive: that is, women who smoke while they are driving.

The safest thing to do, if unfortunately you are threatened with this smiling menace, is to stop at the nearest town and take the train.

[1] This is an undisguised allusion to Paris blocks [pre-1954]. With the English, hooting means making an improper noise. The horn, whose use in France is a duty or a pastime, can be used in England only in emergency. I was in the Major's *Austin of England* in London one day when I felt I should like to smoke. By accident, instead of pressing the cigarette lighter, I leant on the horn. I was at once overwhelmed with withering glances from ten pairs of eyes (not counting the Major's). I wished I could have hidden under the bonnet.

On the road, the English driver, sacrificing safety to courtesy, never takes his eyes off the rear mirror. If he sees another car preparing to pass him he waves him on as soon as the road is clear. No need for a horn. Of course there are the cars coming in the opposite direction at a turn of the road. But the drivers would die rather than hoot. Very often they do die in this way.

FINE SUNDAYS

It is not improper to suppose that if England hasn't been invaded since 1066 it is because foreigners are afraid of having to spend Sunday there.

It is permissible—on comparing the English Sunday which constrains you to boredom with the French Sunday which drives you to enjoyment—to wonder which of the two is the harder to endure.

Many Frenchmen pass the week asking themselves what they will do on Sunday. Sunday usually arrives before they have answered the question. At least that is what happens with the Taupins and the Robillards, who many a time have confessed to me: '*Que voulez-vous?* On Sunday one doesn't know what on earth to do.'

You never suffer from that kind of hesitation in England, where there is hardly anything to do on Sunday except think about what you will do in the week.

To tell the truth I know no more depressed or depressing sight than M. Robillard's Sunday expression as he pushes his latest-born in his pram along the Champs Élysées, giving his eldest a smack because he crossed the road alone, catching hold of the little girl because she doesn't want to cross at all, calling out to Madame who is attracted by the shop windows: 'Are you coming on or not?' reaching the Bois at last in the midst of a stream of walkers whose expression is curiously—I nearly wrote furiously—like his own. All these people who walk, walk on and on, until they reach a certain point where they stop, sit down and begin looking at the people walking towards other points, while those who move on look at the seated ones looking at them passing by.

On Sunday half France looks at the other half.

Parisians in country clothes visit their country cousins disguised for the occasion in their town clothes. The former are astonished at the sight of so much black cloth and so many white collars among the cows and clover; the latter observe with some mistrust these pseudo-English in tweeds.

At the end of fine days, the car-travellers back from the country look with some contempt at the on-foot who have had to be content with the air of the Bois, and who grin jeeringly at this procession of agglutinated cars, asking themselves if you don't have to be a bit dotty to go and join a queue on the by-pass.

TOWN AND COUNTRY SUNDAY-BEST

Meanwhile, the mass of 'sportifs'—those who go to the races and can't understand how anyone can spend a Sunday watching people kick a ball about, and those in the stadiums who wonder what pleasure there can be in entrusting one's money to horses—become momentary allies in a general contempt for their fellow citizens who waste their time on the roads or in the avenues.

In summer, seated on cane-bottomed chairs extracted from their lairs, the concierges lie in wait for, comment upon, and check those returning home.

A few individualists, moved by the spirit of contradiction

rather than by any deep-rooted taste, decide to stay at home and knock in a few nails, tidy up the things they've disarranged, or devote themselves to the national sport of 'pottering about' which consists essentially in making out of old junk and with an expenditure of immense toil articles which can be bought brand new and cheaply over the counter. 'Pottering about' constitutes an activity in France which is so important it deserves special consideration (I shall come back to it). These partisans of Sunday at home correspond in a certain sense to the mass of British citizens who busy themselves with their gardens or with devouring the divorce reports in the many-paged Sunday newspapers, and to lunching as badly as on any other day, only eating rather more.

In His inscrutable caprice the Creator has made us the opposite of our neighbours right up to the last second of the seventh day.

France and England both have two faces, a week-day one and a Sunday one; but the former shows hers while the second hides it.

On Sundays the Frenchman is careful about his dress. The Englishman neglects his. While his French neighbour dresses up, his tendency is rather to undress.[1] On Sundays the Frenchman shaves more carefully. The Englishman—no, there are no two ways of shaving for an Englishman.

While my compatriots get through this day of immobility at home, wearing their shabbiest clothes, leaving it to a few uneducated *nouveaux riches* to dress correctly, the French, all spruced up, come out of their homes, and display themselves in their finest attire: *le costume de Dimanche*. There is no question of Sunday clothes for an Englishman, unless he is entirely without friends or modesty . . . that is to say, a rarity.

The height of *chic* for a Frenchman is to be *tiré à quatre épingles*,[2] an expression which like *s'endimancher* has no real

[1] Except to go to Church, if he does go. Generally, in small towns particularly, the English go to Church not so much for the sake of going but to see who didn't go. (*Major's note.*)

[2] The expressions 'dressed up to the nines' or 'just stepped out of a band box', so difficult to translate, have a slightly derogatory meaning. (*Major's note.*)

equivalent in the language of Shakespeare. Compared with the Englishman who still maintains a sporting air in a *smoking* (dinner jacket) [1] the Frenchman maintains a certain formality in sporting clothes and often in plus fours; he doesn't look quite real—like a new recruit distinguishable at a glance from an old soldier because he has not yet settled into his uniform. Perhaps it's because he is insufficiently trousered.

After all, we must know what we are before knowing what we want to be. We had been playing golf for five hundred years when the French Academy was founded in 1635. Isn't it all to the honour and advantage of the French that they look more natural dressed up as Academicians than as golfers?

Differing from his planetary neighbour who likes to shine like a new penny, the Englishman has a horror of anything new and considers it counterfeit. For him true *chic* is inseparable from a certain shabbiness. Formerly, in the days when Frenchmen gave their old clothes to their servants to finish them off, the English dandies used to make their butlers wear their new suits to break them in. Today the *boys of Belgravia* [2] wear their new suits secretly until they are fit to be seen. The Frenchman will wear his old things until they are absolutely threadbare and keep his new suit for Sunday.

The English way of living six days a week and dying on Sundays may surprise a foreigner, but that of many Frenchmen who merely exist during the week and come to life on Sundays is no less astonishing.

This anxiety to preserve new things and use them—less for himself than for others—only in the last extremity (which means the weekend) is doubtless one of the characteristics of the Frenchman, who would perhaps be getting rusty unless he polished himself up once a week.

My visit to the Turlots was to reveal other aspects of the foreseeing and careful Frenchman.

[1] 'Smoking' in French. I mean, of course, a dinner jacket, but in France you must write English as the French do. (*Major's note.*)

[2] Expression coined by the Major to indicate the district round Belgrave Square, one of the smartest quarters of London.

DIABOLICAL INVENTIONS OF THE FRENCH

THE first time I arrived at Saumur at my friends the Turlots', one summer's day, their house in the Rue Dacier seemed quite dead behind its closed shutters. The servant who opened the door first made me put on some queer felt slippers, perhaps to protect the parquet floor but more likely to make me lose my balance. Then she ushered me in to a fairly large salon impregnated with the smell of mustiness and cretonne. Although the sun filtered through the slats in the shutters, I had to accustom my eyes to the semi-darkness before I could penetrate the surrounding mystery. On all sides were white shapes. I guessed at rather than saw several arm-chairs, a sofa, a grand piano, a chest, something that looked like a harp, all these objects being swathed in dust-sheets. A number of pictures hung on the walls, but it was difficult to know what they represented. Not that they belonged to a peculiarly surrealist school: they were covered with newspaper. The only thing that seemed animated by any movement was the clock. And even its tick-tock came from under a white shroud pierced by the arrow of a bronze Cupid. In a corner over a little table hung two crossed cavalry sabres, both protected by sheaths of yellow linen. I had evidently come at a bad moment: the Turlots were moving. Or they had fallen on evil days and were selling up; the furniture was about to be carted away. My pessimistic suppositions were ended by the appearance of a grey dust-sheet from which emerged the head of the Colonel: 'Forgive me, my dear Major, I was pottering about.'

I have often wondered what the Colonel's 'pottering' really amounted to. Often afterwards I was to find my way into what he called his 'lab' and see him busy with an oscillator and a kind of condenser without, however, guessing what kind of experiments he was conducting. Now I think I can declare that the masterpiece at which he has been working for the last seven years is a wireless set, every bit of which he has assembled with his own hands. It has cost him more than 40,000 francs. On fine days he can hear the programme from the Massif Central. He could get the whole world on a set costing 22,700 francs in any wireless shop. Only a stupid Englishman could fail to notice the difference.

Colonel Turlot's pottering is of the usual handy-man type, but there also exists a *de luxe* pottering, the kind practised by M. Charnelet with his car. As soon as he has bought a car M. Charnelet has one aim: to make it look less like a standard model. With the help of innumerable dealers who each sell him some little thing—a trafficator, reflector mirror, or another badge —saying 'With that it's not just *anybody's* car',[1] M. Charnelet adorns it with all sorts of accessories until when it's re-sprayed it is unrecognizable. Early on Sunday mornings—sometimes on week-days between office hours—he secludes himself and his car in the Bois de Boulogne, brings out his duster, rubs up the chromium, polishes the paintwork, and is annoyed but delighted when an idler prowls round it and finally asks what make it is.

Besides this pottering *de luxe* there is the ordinary, even daily, pottering which is even more fascinating to study: it forms an integral part of the life of every individual. Among its typical manifestations figures the filter, or more precisely the coffee filter. I have often wondered why the Frenchman who could have set before him, ready and hot, the best coffee in the world, prefers to see it drip drop by drop through a mysterious alembic and finally drinks it cold, after burning his fingers in an unsuccessful attempt to regulate the filtering: I can only think he

---

[1] Excellent publicity aid and knock-you-down argument of salesmen in this country where they are always telling you to 'do as everyone else does' but end by persuading you to do as nobody else does. In France they have a horror of being noticed through a panic fear of being ridiculous, but do everything they can to avoid passing unnoticed. The fear of seeming ridiculous (which could not affect an Englishman since, being English, he could not be ridiculous) curbs them, but the desire for manifesting their individuality spurs them on. (*Major's note.*)

TECHNICAL HITCH

likes to 'potter' with his coffee.[1] The filter is one of those discoveries, one of those diabolical inventions of the French which include the 'Minuterie' (pneumatic stair lighting) automatically closing Métro doors, unperforated money orders, scissors for snipping postal orders, and postal orders waiting to be snipped, restrictive electric light switches (either a ceiling light without the bedside light or the bedside light without the ceiling light), and all those creaking cages or cabins which it is very rash to board without reading the OPERATING INSTRUCTIONS, and which, under the name of lifts, achieve the noble distinction of remaining the one means of locomotion which is slower than one's own feet.

Of all the diabolical inventions of the French, one deserves the palm: I refer to those places which the French who love a paradox call 'conveniences' and which they have ingeniously rendered the most inconvenient in the world.[2] First, those in Paris—so intimately connected with the telephone in cafés that sometimes one isn't quite sure what kind of communication one is meant to establish. (The sight of a pale saucer in the middle of which a twenty-franc piece appeals desperately for a sister coin reminds you that you are in the Realm of the Tip.) The country ones—tiny cells which you only reach after fighting your way through a no man's land of hens and old iron—are obscure abysses where you keep your balance only by an acrobatic miracle and where you need all the cunning of a Red Indian to escape the blind vindictiveness of a maelstrom which, in the guise of a flush, makes you bolt for a door so constructed that, instead of opening on to the dry light, it pushes you back into the damp darkness.

---

[1] The same sort of thing happens with books. Any English or American publisher who thought of forcing buyers to cut each section twice along the top and once down the side would soon be bankrupt. In France, on the contrary, certain publishers who wished to make an innovation and present books already cut to the public, had to revert quickly to the old formula which alone could satisfy *real readers*. In the same way, but to a lesser degree, certain real (French) smokers claim that the only real cigarettes are those you make yourself. (*Major's note.*)

[2] Obviously I wouldn't broach such a subject in England, but since I am in the country of Rabelais I think I can take a chance. (*Major's note.*)

Excuse this digression which took me away for a moment. It was necessary. I now come back to Saumur and Colonel Turlot and his dust-sheets and his jobs. Having covered up one of the strange machines in his 'lab' with a camouflage-sheet, probably scrounged from some Allies Surplus Depot, the Colonel took off his overall and hung it on a nail, then extracting his hunter from a washleather case exclaimed: 'Good Lord! twelve o'clock already. Have you seen the Missis?'

We went to look for her. I thought the Colonel was about to produce his wife from a dust-sheet when half of Mme Turlot emerged from a cupboard. Clad in a blue overall, with her head tied up in a scarf, she was putting away a tailor-made with an astrakhan collar in a moth-proof bag.

'Madame's latest extravagance,' said the Colonel. 'Of course she doesn't wear it here except on special occasions. . . . It's really for going to Paris.'

Mme Turlot begged me to excuse her. She really wasn't presentable. She was going to put on a dress and get ready for lunch. I was sorry my arrival had obviously thrown the household into a state of some perturbation. The Turlots, who have a large house, were preparing to lunch in the kitchen, but in my honour undertook to deshroud the dining-room and the famous haunted salon with its spectral furniture into which they never ventured when they were alone.

'We'll open a nice bottle for you, my dear Major,' said the Colonel, who owns a very good cellar but drinks every day a red *vin ordinaire*.

It may seem dangerous to judge a country by appearances, especially when that is hidden under a dust-sheet, and I have no doubt that the French in general make a less systematic use of the dust-sheet than the Turlots do. But leaving aside the Colonel, I cannot help remembering that M. Taupin, like M. Charnelet, has only one thought when he buys a car: to put loose covers over the seats. They remove these the day they sell the car (*perf. cond.*) and if possible use them again in their new one.

I am inclined to believe that the dust-cover is the symbol of the saving—even self-depriving—spirit of the French. These people, who are so greedy of possessions that they will say 'I have my poor' [1] and are more spoiled by life than any others on earth, make a veritable cult of hardship, covering up the seats of their cars being one of its most widespread manifestations. I know of a millionaire who made a reputation by taking his meals on a deal table, sending his children to the village school, travelling third class, never cutting a piece of string, and saying to any of his employees who asked for a rise: 'I can't think how you manage to spend so much!'

In the land of plenty the real, most solid wealth attires itself in humility: only poor people spend recklessly. [2]

---

[1] Compare this expression with the 'I always give to the Salvation Army', loudly proclaimed by M. Charnelet when a salvationist in a blue bonnet comes into the restaurant. Obviously M. Charnelet wants to emphasize his discernment in giving. Direct contact with a down-and-out, especially in a restaurant, makes him uneasy, but the uniform of the Salvation Army is reassuring: he knows where his money goes. (*Major's note.*)

[2] To these must be added a few super-rich foreigners whose extravagance, while considered reasonable if it is a question of restoring Versailles, are far more criticized if it's a question of a private fête by night. Yet the strange thing is, in this realm of mistrust and the old stocking, where it is the custom to put something by for bad times, and when the bad times come to continue putting something by for worse ones, there is nothing like a foreigner for getting money out of its hiding places. The people mistrust investments, but at regular intervals we learn that a man whose name ends in *ski* or *vici*, more powerful than any Dupont, has got millions out of them and ruined three centuries of saving. '*It was a long way off . . . no one would ever know*', say the dupes who (always this fear of appearing ridiculous) are careful not to make themselves known when the question of indemnity arises, but settle down this time to depriving themselves in good earnest. (*Major's note.*)

THE LAND OF MIRACLES

THE Miracle, together with the vine, is one of the principal products of France.

All Frenchmen—positivists, rationalists or Voltairians—firmly believe in miracles. When the enemy is at the gates of Paris, or when there is only a minute left to play against England at Colombes, then they rely on Providence, who, it must be admitted, has often spoiled them.

Having, like her Latin sisters, subscribed to miracles from her earliest childhood, France attracts miracles as other countries attract humidity. More than that. She adapts them to the needs of the moment: the miracle which went on foot with Saint Geneviève, on horseback with Joan of Arc, became motorized with the taxis of the Marne. Tomorrow it may be atomic.

In other countries, when a statesman cries 'Only a miracle can save us', that's the end of everything. In France it can be the beginning of a great many things. The Frenchman brightens up in darkness, becomes organized in chaos. Possible things do not interest him very much: impossible things impassion him. In the land of facility difficulty is inspiring. The national flower, astuteness, thrives on it.

The miracle follows a Frenchman through life just as it accompanies France throughout her history. The first thing the French (who are cultivated even before they are born) teach their children is that they were discovered in a cabbage. Parents do everything in their power to make their children become miracle-children. Brought up as they are in contact with learned provincial spinsters, indulgent uncles, and philosophic old men, the children of France, very forward for their age, deliver themselves of octogenarian opinions which would drive English parents crazy, but delight the authors of their days who enjoy airing them in public, like an anthology of witty sayings.

The child, on his side, openly or in secret, keeps up this miracle cult. He learns not only of Joan of Arc, and the natural frontiers the Creator marked out for the French, while He left so many others to discover them for themselves [1]; he associates with those heroes of radio, film and comic strip, who find their way through virgin forests, rescue a few (English) explorers from certain death, and come back to France with the secret of the curare bomb, and congratulations from Scotland Yard.

The astuteness of the schoolboy continues to increase until it allows him to perform the miracle known to all Frenchmen—the famous Miracle of the little Broom. In the barracks courtyard, under the vigilant eye of the resolutely unhelpful sergeant, he produces from nowhere a little broom to sweep away the wind. These are the miniature peace-time Battles of the Marne. The Frenchman retains the imprint of this scholasticism till the day of his death, and transmits it to his son, saying, 'You'll see when you do your military service'.

Side by side with the lycée and the barracks, the technical schools take charge of the sharpening and embellishing of the Frenchman's astuteness, and he emerges from them as from a conjurer's box of tricks; he grasps at once what so many others understand too late. Sometimes he leaves the country. Then he installs the Métro at Caracas, or introduces frogs to the cuisines of Adelaide. He brings Gascony to Cincinnati, the Polytechnic to Kabul. But he will retire as early as possible to Barcelonette or Brie, because, though there may be many countries for earning one's living, France is, after all, the one where life is best spent.

Land of Miracles, miracle-men, miracle-dresses, Realm of Fine Shades and Imponderables, I am about to leave you. . . .
Soon now I shall fly off to Bengal at the cordial invitation of

[1] From this point of view, as from so many others, England is of course a land apart. Still I could find no answer to M. Taupin's very strange remark calling my attention to the fact that the first two letters of the word France were those of the English word for liberty: in English (*freedom*), in German (*freiheit*), in Swedish (*frihet*), in Icelandic (*frolsi*), not to mention other languages, and that all this was a sign of some miraculous order of things. (*Major's note.*)

E

'LOOK, ELMER, A STATUE OF INGRID BERGMAN!'

my old friend Colonel Basil Cranworth who, before taking up his new post at Singapore, has asked me to his last tiger shoot. But I shall not set off as I used to do. A hundred faces, invisible yet present, escort me. Colonel Cranworth and our host the Maharajah of Bhagalpur will not be aware of them, but, while they are talking about man-eaters, Martine's face will hover over the table, I shall think of Martine, I shall think of Paris. And my longing will not only be sentimental. In India, some months ago now, one night I felt the gastric nostalgia of France creeping over me. As I slept in my tent in the torrid monsoon-swept jungle of Assam, old mother Grenouillet appeared to me in a dream: 'What are you up to there, Major?' Standing beside the peaceful waters which know neither monsoon nor typhoon, with her hands on her hips, she asked: 'What would you say, Major, to some of my trout *à la crème*?'

That night I knew I was a changed man.

Yes, it's done now! Whether I'm with the Sikhs or the Zulus, at Rangoon or in Zanzibar, I think of the Place Vendôme and Azay-le-Rideau. And when I come back from India or Kalahari, and the aeroplane, after flying over so many stretches of sand and rock where earth and sky seem to have declared war on one another, brings me nearer the winding Seine, over that little hexagon blessed by the Gods, where everything is done for man's pleasure on man's scale, for the greater delight of his retina, his palate and his heart, I know I have come back to the Land of Miracles.

Country, unlike any other, whose farms, churches and country houses fit so well into the landscape that they all seem to have been conceived at the same time.

Land of forty-three million thinking planets, each with its own little idea at the back of its mind, whose citizens—all different and all alike in wanting to be different—argue ceaselessly and in the end conclude:

'Fundamentally we are agreed. . . .'

Country where the people's individuality is so marked that they cannot hear a weather report on the wireless without identifying themselves, joyously with 'set fair', dramatically with 'stormy'.

Strange land, where in one and the same minute I can find someone who hates me and someone who loves me, and realize—and that's the miracle—that they are one and the same person.

Charnelets and Taupins, Turlots and Pochets, all animated by the same spirit of criticism and freedom—I have often spoken ill of you.

Now I must earn your forgiveness.

I have said that you were sceptical, mistrustful, parsimonious. The miracle is that you are also equally enthusiastic, trustful, generous. If tomorrow you were to become disciplined, accurate, silent, a great misfortune would have befallen the world. For your faults are but the reverse side of your qualities. Your nation of xenophobes is a refuge for foreigners, you don't resist fraud yet you bring up your children in the cult of the right road, your race of *petits bourgeois* is a race of *grands seigneurs*, you are the most inhospitable people in the whole universe, and your country the most welcoming on the globe. And if it be true that minds are like parachutes (as Lord Dewar said, to function they must be open), then you are the world's finest parachutists.

Forgive me. . . . Forgive my audacity. Looking back over these notes of an explorer who set out to discover France and the French, I am terrified by my temerity. . . . What right had I—an Englishman—to catalogue your weaknesses? The miserable right of men who think they are qualified to speak about life on earth while they are mere children when they die, without even having lived to be a hundred? Perhaps simply by the right I learnt from Bernard Shaw: the best way to familiarize yourself with a subject is to write a book about it.

It remains for me to obtain the forgiveness of my Queen.

That good English governess Miss ffyfth teaches the children of the Bois de Boulogne that they are very lucky to be French, for they inhabit the one country in the world which is only twenty-one miles away from England.

May my Sovereign pardon me if I now reverse the axiom: one of the Englishman's privileges is that he need only cross the Channel to be in France. May Her Gracious Majesty not hold it against me that I have chosen to live in France. Was it not in my humble way the best I could do to celebrate the *Entente Cordiale?*

Alas! There is more to come, your Majesty, and worse. Nowadays I dawdle in the streets of Paris. . . . When a car runs into another car (and God knows that happens often enough) I stand and stare. . . . Then again—dare I admit?—such charming silhouettes pass along the Paris streets, especially in spring . . . that . . . yes, I find myself turning round. For forty years I saw, now I look. That is not all: the other day, forgetting all my reserve, I allowed myself to ask M. Taupin about that spot on his nose. And when I left him I said '*Au revoir, allez!*' Finally, my Queen, there's that terrible longing for snails that may come over me at Gibraltar or in Bombay, or for that Chambolle– Musigny which old Rougetrogne fetches up from his cellar when I go to Avallon, and which brings out the blue line of my temples against the crimson background of my cheeks so marvellously that the *patron* calls to his little boy, 'Sonny, come and see Major Thompson doing the Union Jack'. Good Heavens, how disgraceful, your Majesty! I am indeed damned. God will punish me one day by making me disintegrate on the banks of the Cousin or the Midouze.

Meanwhile I confess: hills of Burgundy, blue distances of the Île de France, quays of Paris, provinces of Saint-Louis en l'Île, I am your docile slave.

O France! where we can put up so comfortably and have such good meals, how often now have I unfolded your map with its names so full of promise: Brocéliande, Vézelay, Brantôme, Loctudy, and all those anonymous but individual La Fertés with the old maids gossiping behind the curtains, and all the pretty girls who seem to have been created just to give the old maids something to gossip about. . . . O France! I love your speech, I love your sky, I love your light, I love your stubborn spirit.

I love everything about you and you in everything.

F for folly, *r* for reason, *a* for amour, *n* for nanny, *c* for chauvin, *e* for Ernest, . . . I love France.

MAJOR THOMPSON AND I

Translated from the French

by

W. MARM

C.S.I., D.S.O., O.B.E.

'BUT MAJOR, *THAT* ISN'T FRANCE AT ALL!'

(Translator's Foreword)

SOME of our readers may be wondering how on earth I came to help my good friend, Pierre Daninos, to write a book about Anglo-Saxons —a race of mortals whom, I need hardly add, no Frenchman can ever really understand. Well, it all began one day when I was walking past the French National Assembly with Pochet. Pointing my umbrella at the pillared façade, I said to him:

'Now then, what do you think of your Chamber?'

'*My* Chamber? *Mon cher Major*, you know perfectly well it isn't "*my*" Chamber".'

'But it's the Chamber of all the French people. Didn't you vote?'

'Naturally. But look, Major, *that* isn't France at all!'

For Pochet—and the same goes for Taupin—France is never *that* at all. France isn't three million Socialists. It isn't two million Radicals, nor three million Independent Peasants. Nor, obviously, is it five million Communists. And good lord! who would dream of suggesting that it might be fifty-two Poujadiste deputies? As for that Parisian couple I bumped into last election day on the ski-slopes in Switzerland and who made it quite clear they were not bothering to vote, how could I ever have thought that that was *la France*? Only a subversive wretch could entertain such a notion. Just as only a damned fool could confuse France with those young conscripts who recently held up their train on their way from the barracks. As Colonel

Turlot said to me: 'A handful of rookies! We'll soon get them back into line! France, the real France, isn't that at all!'

It was the same story the day those strikers at Orly forced me to leave the plane just as it was going to take off for London, and to flounder about in the dark, because they had not received their previous day's strike pay. Here again I was given to understand by Pochet that this was all the work of a handful of trouble-makers. *Voyons, donc*, that wasn't France at all!

'France, Major, is a country that works! Take a trip up North and you'll have something to write home about!' said my friend, without realizing that this was precisely the direction of my intended journey. 'You'll see . . . they're at their desks while you're still in bed!'

Pochet was so persuasive that it was I who suffered from a guilt complex on leaving the airport from which they were ejecting me. I must say that Pochet seemed a trifle upset by the whole business. On our way back to Paris in his car he jumped a red traffic light. A *gendarme* stopped him and ticked him off. Pochet kept unusually quiet, but once we were on our way again, he smiled.

'Too bad about that summons,' I said. He made a deprecating gesture. 'It'll be washed out—I've got a friend at the Prefecture of Police!'

I asked him if this was standard French practice.

'Fortunately not. It would all be too easy otherwise! You've got to know somebody, *violà!*'

I was reminded by this incident of some French motorists I had helped last summer, when I turned round and went back ten kilometres to get them a mechanic. Curious thing—they insisted on inviting me to dinner the next time I passed through their town. '*Mais si, Monsieur*, we insist, it's so rare to find people on the road who are so considerate, and a foreigner at that—all the more reason!' But how in heaven's name could I take them for authentic Frenchmen since when I was back in their town and telephoned they told me themselves that they weren't there?

Yes, you have to be blissfully naïve—as only the naïve

Englishman that I am can be—to make generalizations about
the French, particularly after a Paris bus conductor has said to
you (as happened one day when I couldn't produce the right
fare):

'If you haven't any change, why don't you stay at home?'
After which he grumbled his way through the bus muttering:
'*Encore un Amerloque!*' [1]

Only a simpleton would think that France is *that* and over-
look its people's characteristic courtesy. Still, it was my distinct
impression that the bus was full of Frenchmen, for shortly after
the conductor's outburst we got caught in a traffic jam and I
heard someone exclaim:

'The first thing I'd do would be to get those fat foreign cars
off the road to leave room for people to move!'

But I was doubtless mistaken and in fact it must have been a
Yemenite bus that I boarded at the Porte Saint Martin. For
when I told Pochet about it, he said:

'*Soyons sérieux, Major!* . . . France, after all, isn't a bus! You
may have had a spot of bother with an ill-humoured bus conductor, but you know as well as I do that France doesn't behave
like that.'

It really is amazing how wrong one can be about France!
The other day, for example, when Taupin was taking me to see
one of his friends, he advised me:

'Call him *Monsieur le Président*. It will please him no end.'

'Of course,' I said, 'but *Président* of what?'

'Well,' said Taupin, 'he's the *Vice Président* of the Limoges
chapter of the Skins and Hides Guild.'

'In that case, shouldn't I call him *Monsieur le Vice Président*?'

'Anything but that!' cried Taupin. 'It's like calling someone
"Lieutenant-Colonel".'

I was reminded that I had that very same day met the President
of the Virgin Cinematographic Film Guild and the President of
the Moquette Bird Orphanage, and I began to wonder if every
Frenchman wasn't the President of something.

'*Mais non*,' Taupin told me. 'I am, as it happens, the
_____
[1] French slang for 'Another Yank!'

President of Les Amis de la Pédale Gasco-Béarnaise.[1] But that
doesn't mean that all Frenchmen are like that.'

Can it be that the French are never 'like that'?

When—to cite another example—I walk into the waiting-
room of that good dentist, or perhaps I should say, stomato-
logist, Dr Dusseloup, and find that there is only one weekly
there I can get my teeth into—a copy of the *Petit Explorateur
Français*, reporting the activities of the Botanical Garden of
Tananarive in the year 1898—the doctor explains to me:

'*Que voulez-vous, Major?* I can only keep the old magazines—
the rest get pinched.'

When I complain to the manageress of the Hôtel des Flots
Bleus because there is only one coat-hanger in my bedroom
wardrobe (stolen, at that, by some transient from the Schweizer-
hof in Lucerne), she says to me: 'People are always going off
with them.'

Or when I suggest to the *patron* of the Petit Gastronome that
he might at least put a box of paper towels in his toilets, he has a
ready-made answer: 'They wouldn't stay there one hour!'

All this makes me think that a foreigner who limited his tour
of France to visiting a dentist, a restaurant and an hotel might
easily come away with the idea that the French are a nation of
kleptomaniacs who are wary of pickpockets, particularly when
they come to England armed with the family *Guide Bleu*.

But it was useless trying to explain all this to Pochet.

'Frankly, Major, you exaggerate,' he protested. 'The French
are not thieves.'

Wishing just at that moment to knock out my pipe, I was
handed by Pochet an ashtray inscribed: 'Excelsior Palace Hotel,
Roma.'

'Souvenir of a trip,' he offered by way of explanation.

But I had the impression he blushed.

All the same, how wrong one can be about the French! Why,
only yesterday I was waiting in a rather dark and smelly corner
for a young lady to finish her call in a telephone kiosk (which, I

[1] Literally *The Friends of the Gascon–Bearnais Pedal*—one of France's innumerable provincial cycling clubs.

'ALL RIGHT, I MUST BE OFF . . . THERE'S A CHAP WAITING, WISH YOU
COULD SEE HIS FACE!'

must say, was covered with the most shocking inscriptions).
Every now and then the door would open slightly and I would
hear her say: '*Allez, je te laisse . . . y a un type qui attend, j'vou-
drais qu'tu voies sa bille! . . . Alors on se voit ce soir? . . . Allez,
au revoir!*' [1] I'd think she'd finished, but the door would close
again and the conversation would carry on. Do the French spend
their time ringing themselves up to say that they'll see each other
and seeing each other to say that they'll ring each other up?

'But no,' Pochet protested when I told him about this. 'It was
a woman, Major! *Ah, les femmes! . . .* All the same, that's not
France!'

What in heaven's name *is* France?

When I finally put the question to Pochet and Taupin neither
of them took very kindly to it. Both treated my mild prodding
as a kind of personal affront. Pochet remarked rather heatedly
that my artful questioning—an '*interrogation sournoise*' he called
it—was a typical example of 'Anglo-Saxon hypocrisy'. As for
Taupin, he attributed my 'outburst' to passing ill-humour
brought on by a row I had just had with my wife Martine over
those long woollies I insisted on wearing.[2] He followed this up
by accusing me of being out of sorts because Martine and I
couldn't agree on the proper schooling to be given our second
son, Nicholas. Yet Taupin, like Pochet, knows perfectly well
that scolding a people as the headmaster does a schoolboy isn't
England at all!

[1] Colloquial French (not that of the Academy) which might be roughly translated: 'All right, I must be off . . . there's a chap waiting, wish you could see his
face! . . . We'll meet this evening then? . . . All right, goodbye!'

[2] Let me explain, even by adding a footnote to my own preface, just what all
the fuss was about. It was all a lamentable consequence of my being held up that
night by those strikers at Orly, with the result that I caught a frightful cold and
had to take refuge inside a pair of those heavy woollies which permit quinqua-
genarians like myself to brave the elements in mid-January without an overcoat.
Besides, it's a gross overstatement to say I had a 'row' with Martine. At most
there took place an *échange de mots*, as the French so aptly put it. I put in a word
with Martine and she exchanges it against half a dozen of her own, and at a much
faster pace. I'm pretty used to it now. But what I can't get used to is the tone of
command she adopts with regard to things as personal and private as my pants.
'Do take off those frightful long pants, Marminet, I entreat you, and put on your
overcoat!' I ask you: is this the sort of thing a former officer in the Indian Army
should put up with? Definitely not.

But to get back to the point of this foreword. Having failed to make much headway with Pochet and Taupin, I thought I would turn to my old friend Daninos and see if he could do any better at enlightening me as to what France, the real France, really is. He listened to me, I'm afraid, with growing impatience and then exploded.

'Major! I've had enough of your sarcastic gibes at the French! For two whole years I've put up with your *British rule*. . . . I offered you my help with your notes about France and the French and all I got out of it was your grudging permission to slip in an occasional footnote in which I could speak up for my compatriots. . . . But now I've had enough! Put down your pen and since you're on the warpath, take up your rifle——'

'Express Magnum 375——'

'All right, take the express if you want to and go back to India. . . . But with your permission I'm going to do a little travelling of my own. In fact, Major, I've a mind to visit England—and perhaps even go and see your distant cousins in America—so that I can report in my turn just what *you* are like or not like!'

'Now, don't get excited, Daninos,' I said. 'Where is your self-control? As a matter of fact, it's not a bad idea. But——'

'But what?'

'Well,' I said, trying to put it as tactfully as possible, 'you really don't mean to say you're going to write a book all by yourself.'

'It's something I've done already.'

'Yes, old boy, but it wasn't a book about Anglo-Saxons.'

'All right, Major, I'll get Pochet to help me . . . and Sonia too, for that matter.'

Great scott! I thought.

'And what about me?' I remonstrated. 'You really can't object to my coming with you when you visit the British Isles, just as you accompanied me on my sentimental journey through France . . . Yes, and it wouldn't be such a bad idea, either, to let me put a word in now and again whenever you find yourself getting a little out of your depth.'

'All right, Major, have it your own way. But I shan't be so selfish as you were. I'll gladly yield you the pen—and not just for the footnotes . . . but, on occasion, if you feel like it, for whole pages at a time.'

'It's a bargain!' I said. 'You go on over to London ahead of me. In a couple of weeks my dear wife and I will be at our place in Hampshire—it's always easier and quieter at home. We can discuss more calmly our son's education. But as you're going over first, I suggest that after spending a night or two in an hotel you move over to my old friend, Mrs Cripplestone's. Her boarding-house will give you a splendid opportunity for exploring a little corner of England. So cheerio, old man—and good luck!'

And that's how it all started.

i

'BUT ENGLAND, MAJOR, ISN'T *THAT* EITHER!'

 Tᴇɴ minutes on the soil of Albion was enough to make me realize that England was not at all what Major Thompson claimed.

As I boarded the London boat-train at Dover, I tried to keep in mind the essential rules of British conduct which the Major had carefully instilled in me:

1. The English never speak to anyone unless they have been properly introduced (except in case of shipwreck).

2. You must never talk about God or your stomach.

Yet at lunch the very first Englishman I met was seated opposite me, and instead of saying 'No, thank you' when I passed him the pickles, as a Frenchman would have done, exclaimed:

'I wish to god I dare eat those blessed pickles—but I've got a stomach ulcer!'

I felt the Major's world reel and the very foundations of the Empire rock under my feet. I could almost hear the Major's voice expostulating:

'Of course, that was a very inferior type of Englishman. . . . That's not England, Daninos!'

Now I'm certainly not going to claim here and now that all Englishmen take God's name in vain and talk to strangers about their stomachs, but if France seemed to the Major a country of forty-three million exceptions, I can safely say that Great Britain is an island made up of fifty-three million islets; for I have never met an Englishman who did not speak of his countrymen as though he himself were quite unlike them.

Actually, one of the hardest things, when you get to London, is to meet an Englishman. It's even harder in English history, in the making of which so many peoples have had a hand. At times you have to wait six hundred years before running across a king who wasn't born in Osnabrück, Hanover, or Blois. The Canutes were Danes, the Plantagenets French, the Tudors Welsh, the Stuarts Scotch, and finally, after booting out a Scotsman to make way for a Dutchman, the English treated themselves to a German king who couldn't speak a word of English.[1]

Without going all the way back to drag in William the Conqueror, the first cab driver I had in London kept up an incessant tirade against the English in a curious foreign accent. At every traffic light he grumbled and spouted bits of the *Daily Worker*. As we were driving by Buckingham Palace, he said to me over his shoulder:

'Ever thought of the number of cabbies they could put up in there?'

I said, No. I had never considered Buckingham Palace from that angle. Surprised by such irreverence, I asked him why as an Englishman he didn't feel more attached to the Crown.

'I'm British, not English,' he said. 'I'm a Welshman.'

I thought I might have better luck at the hotel meeting a really authentic Englishman, but the manager proved to be Swiss, the desk clerk Belgian, the lift boy Malayan, the chambermaids Irish, the *maître d'hôtel* (and of course the chef) French and the waiters Italian.

The evening of my second day, having still not found an Englishman, I decided to take the matter up with the manager, Mr Wenger Stücki: 'I take it the owner is English,' I said.

'No, Monsieur. Mr MacNamara, the owner of the chain of Elizabethan Hotels, is Scotch.'

It's a serious mistake to think that England has never been occupied since 1066. She still is—by the Scots. They crossed the border of the Union in 1707 and have never gone back again. The Scots are a people who never really feel at home except at somebody else's—particularly when the somebody else is Eng-

---

[1] For heaven's sake! What does all this prove? A Turk can perfectly well be King of England. If we install him in Buckingham Palace, it's because he suits us, that's all. We don't ask him for his identity card (which, I might add, didn't exist before this last war and doesn't now). (W. M. T.)

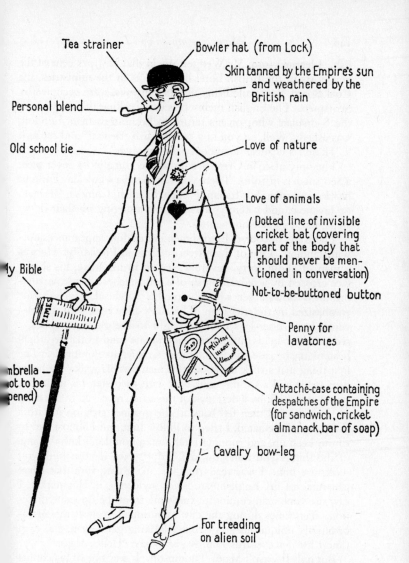

Tea strainer

Bowler hat (from Lock)

Skin tanned by the Empire's sun and weathered by the British rain

Personal blend

Old school tie

Love of nature

Love of animals

Dotted line of invisible cricket bat (covering part of the body that should never be mentioned in conversation)

Not-to-be-buttoned button

Penny for lavatories

ly Bible

mbrella — ot to be pened)

Attaché-case containing despatches of the Empire (for sandwich, cricket almanack, bar of soap)

Cavalry bow-leg

For treading on alien soil

X-RAY PHOTOGRAPH OF MR W. M. T . . . ., BRITISH CITIZEN

lish. I learned from Mr Wenger Stücki that 72·5 per cent of the
key posts in the British hotel business, as in the ministries, the
Coal Board, the textile firms and the railways, were occupied by
Scotsmen. The English themselves enjoy telling the story about
the Scotsman who, on his return to Edinburgh from London,
was asked: 'Well, so you saw our English friends?' and replied:
'Hadn't a chance. I saw only the top men.'

The only place in Great Britain where you almost never meet
a Scotsman is in Soho. There you can spend a whole day without
hearing anything but Italian, French, Spanish, Chinese, German,
or Javanese, and where you see people lounging on their doorsteps, like vulgar Continentals.

There are, of course, Englishmen in London, appearances notwithstanding. One of them overtook me in Piccadilly. He was
a man of about forty, severely elegant in his attire, his scarlet
face crossed by a reddish bush of a moustache, a black narrow-
brimmed bowler set squarely on his forehead, his waistline
emphasized by the smart cut of his navy-blue coat with its side-
vents, his trouser-legs falling straight to the gleaming shoes, a
red carnation in his button-hole, and in one hand a small weather-
beaten attaché case and in the other a rapier-like umbrella. The
first thing that struck me about this man was his walk. He had a
firm stride and a springy gait, and with each step his umbrella,
raised chin-high by a deft flick of the wrist, revolved in the palm
of his hand and then fell back to the ground, striking it with a
sharp rap. Fascinated, I tried to follow him, but I almost had to
run to keep up, and running after a man you don't know is one
of the things you don't do in London, even if you think you
recognize him. I was ready to give up, feeling sure that I had
lost track of my Englishman, when suddenly, in Haymarket, I
saw the same man coming towards me from the opposite direction. Ten times during the day I continued to meet this extra-
ordinarily ubiquitous and striking-looking gentleman, and each
time I hurried towards him, ready to say: 'Hello, Major!'

But no! It wasn't Major Thompson. It was one of his countless brothers. London is a city where hundreds of thousands of
bowlers, all planted on the same heads, advance to the conquest

A PUZZLE FOR POCHET, WHO HAD ARRANGED TO MEET THE MAJOR
AT PICCADILLY

of the same invisible goals. There are not in all the world other men who march towards their destiny so impassive and secure in their own right as do the Londoners.

And just what is this destiny? For a long time I asked myself this question. Just what state secrets, just what *most secret despatches* do these long-legged Edens carry about with them in their attaché cases?

One day I decided to follow one of them to the bitter end. Emerging from the Foreign Office, the black bowler turned into Whitehall, walked up the Mall, and then disappeared into the Tube at St James's Park. Thanks to some special training I managed to keep up with him. He began by reading *The Times*, but as we got farther from the West End and he found he had a whole seat to himself, he folded away his paper, placed his precious baggage on his knees, and cautiously opened it. At last I was to be let into the secret of a Foreign Office attaché case!

The despatches of the Empire on this particular day consisted of a bar of soap, a small white napkin, the *Cricket Almanack* recognizable by its cover, and a ham sandwich, which the gentleman consumed, just as though he were travelling from Angoulême to Poitiers. I must admit he ate it very daintily. But the fact remains he ate.

A little later I told the Major of my discovery.

'Don't tell me, you confounded Frenchman,' he cried, 'that you are now going to believe that Foreign Office despatch cases carry nothing in them but *casse-croûte*, to use your own rather vulgar expression!' [1]

'Well, no . . . But still, nothing so resembles one Englishman in a bowler hat as another Englishman in a bowler hat.[2] The

[1] *Casse-croûte* is a French term literally meaning 'break-crust', much as we say 'break-fast'. It is used to designate the traditional chunk of bread, accompanied by cheese or ham and often by the classic bottle of wine, which the French working man (or woman) carries to work. (W. M. T.)

[2] For the benefit of the Major and those of my readers who think I've made all this up, I might add that several weeks later when I told some English friends of this incident they pulled out a copy of a women's magazine and showed me a letter in the Correspondence Column which ran: 'The other day in the street I found an elegant gentleman in a bowler hat, striped trousers and a black waistcoat walking alongside of me carrying an umbrella and an attaché case. All of a

philosopher J. B. Lowell himself once said: 'Never do I give thanks to Providence more gladly than the day it makes me meet an Englishman who is unlike the rest.'

Whence springs this similarity?

The English can be explained by their Anglo-Saxon heritage and the influence of the Methodists. But I prefer to explain them in terms of tea, roast beef and rain. A people is first of all what it eats, drinks and gets pelted with. Men who are ceaselessly being battered by the wind and the rain and shrouded in a permanent fog end up themselves turning into raincoats, which shed criticism as easily as water off an oilskin. Men who drink tea seven times a day and eat the same vegetables and meats all year round naturally end up with the same rosy complexions. There is roast beef in the Englishman just as there is rice in the Chinese.[1]

Indeed, how can one understand such people? How define people who make a point of never asking personal questions about their neighbours' private lives, but follow all the goings and comings and new acquisitions of their Queen as though they were the *concierges* of Buckingham Palace; who are stout champions of individual liberty, but forbid you to touch a drop of alcohol after 3 p.m.; who don't like to talk, but adore orators; who hate heat, but love a good fire;[2] who have an innate sense of grandeur, but who—from their cottages and ponies to their railway engines—carefully cultivate the small; who talk of trifles

---

sudden his case struck a lamp-post and out spilled its contents—two lettuces!' Think of it! The same attaché case episode—twice in one year! There must be something in this after all. . . .

[1] For once I find myself agreeing. If Frenchmen differ so much from one another, it's because one likes to sample his snails, while another savours his meat *pâté*, and the wife of the third brews him his pet stew—his *petit pot-au-feu à lui*—which is quite unlike the neighbour's. I'm never as rosy-hued as I am in France about 3 p.m., and goodness knows! the Union Jack which you claim to find all over my face is differently shaded at Nuits Saint-Georges from what it is at Saumur. Your French Côtes du Rhône, your Clos Vougeots, and your Muscadets give the French an infinite variety of coloration. Tea and whisky condemn the British to greater uniformity. But apart from that, you simply can't understand us. (W. M. T.)

[2] There is perhaps no more delicate pleasure for an Englishman than to sit in a lively draught in an Elizabethan or Tudor drawing-room freezing his spine while he roasts his face in the hearth.

POCHET IN HYDE PARK, 'NOW MOVE ALONG 'ERE! 'OW WOULD YOU
LIKE TO BE LOOKED AT LIKE THAT?'

when sober and begin to talk of serious things when drinking; who do things like no one else in the world and yet are astonished that the rest of the world doesn't do the same; who consider *The Times* the most serious newspaper in the world, but reserve its front page for personal messages from gentlemen seeking travelling companions; who see their children caned by their masters without batting an eyelid but cannot stand the sight of a crippled sparrow; who are suspicious of everything that isn't British, but who derive their national beverage from a Chinese–Indian shrub; who wouldn't dream of kissing in public in the Tube or in the street, but who do it at Hyde Park or Maidenhead before a public that's twice as large; who abhor cross-breeding but are themselves an extraordinary cross-mixture of Celts, Saxons, Scandinavians and Normans; who reproach the French for living to eat, but spend their time nibbling odds and ends; who dress informally in their country houses, but insist no donning grey bowler hats and carnations before going to inspect the udder of a Yorkshire cow at an exhibition; who remain the cradle of the most unbending conservatism but served as the incubator for Karl Marx and Lenin; who enforce austerity on the Sabbath while distributing a Sunday newspaper scandal to eight million readers; who manufacture *bidets* for the rest of the world, but won't have one in the house; [1] who carry an umbrella when the sun is out and a raincoat when it pours; who are always chanting 'Home, Sweet Home!' but love to settle down abroad; who wouldn't for the world talk about their stomachs, but who advertise contraceptives in their chemist shops; who are regarded as the paragons of politeness but who walk into restaurants ahead of their wives. . . .

'Nonsense!' the Major cried, when I cited this last practice as an evident breach of manners. 'We do that for the sake of feminine modesty—to protect our defenceless women against strangers.'

---

[1] From Bruges to Zanzibar you can find bathrooms equipped with an impressive array of *bidets* bearing the trademark Shanks & Co. Ltd., of Barrhead, Scotland. But in Barrhead, Scotland, you will look for one in vain. Great Britain reserves this item for export to savages.

'All right. . . . But can you deny, you who are reputed to be the best brought up people in the world, that your cabinet ministers govern at Westminster with their feet upon the mace table of the House of Commons?'

'That's a question of privilege, my dear Daninos, not boorishness.'

Major Thompson is always right, even when everything conspires to prove him wrong. Here is another of the Englishman's great strengths. He has a ready-made explanation for all those inconsistencies of his countrymen which I can only sum up in the word used by the Major to define the French—contradiction.[1]

[1] Once again this French mania for wanting to explain everything! We English are either far too canny or too thickheaded to try to understand ourselves. Every year, for the past thousand, a foreigner returns home from England with a book intended to explain the English to his countrymen. And that simply proves that not one of them has yet succeeded. There's a good reason for it too. An Englishman cannot be explained; he can only be taken for granted. The English are like electricity: they exist without anyone being able to explain it or them. (W. M. T.)

CATASTROPHE AT MRS CRIPPLESTONE'S

For me the history of England really began upon the day I blew up the bathroom water-heater in Mrs Cripplestone's most respectable Victorian establishment. Had I but known from the start that this strange cylinder of copper looking like a cross between a boa constrictor and a flame-thrower was called a *geyser*, I should have been on my guard, and I should not have neglected to follow the directions more carefully. But these are things you only learn when the damage is done. In England a foreigner only finds out what should be done after doing what he shouldn't.

It may seem childish to start English history with the explosion of a water-heater. Most historians prefer to date it from another catastrophe—the defeat of Harold, King of England, by William the Conqueror in 1066, a year which the British by one of those strange quirks which so mystify the foreigner consider the most glorious in their history. But quite apart from the fact that it is indispensable for anyone really wishing to get to know Great Britain to visit one of those boarding-houses where spinsters write personal letters to the editor of *The Times* offering their advice on the castration of cats, or trying to make fortunes by betting—half-heartedly—on French racehorses at Ascot, it is often easier to explain England by the absence of central heating than by the presence of the Plantagenets.

The golden age of British comfort, on the renown of which the British still live, dates from 43 B.C. In those days Britain could boast both Romans and central heating. The two disappeared at about the same time—the first never to return, the second to be re-adopted only with great hesitancy, usually by owners of blocks of flats or cosmopolitan hotels of rather dubious repute.

Now nothing, you might think, could be more impersonal than a water-heater. On the continent, no doubt—but English water-heaters are not like others. Like the English themselves, they always keep something from you. Of course, if you get to know them well after a goodish lapse of time, they can become the best friends in the world and tepedize your water up to a cosy 55 degrees. But if the very first day you meet them you become too familiar, pry too much into their secrets and try to light them up like some vulgar continental water-heaters, their susceptibilities are offended and they slap you down. You just have to remember that you are in a land of compromise; and just as the Anglican Church is a compromise between catholicism and protestantism, so the hot water of British boarding-houses is a compromise between ice and steam.

There are, to be sure, plenty of hotels in London where the water is as piping hot as on the continent. If you are going to England to wash, you had better stay at the Savoy. But that wasn't my sole aim in crossing the Channel, and the Major was perfectly right in advising me to put up at his friend Mrs Cripple-stone's, in South Kensington, in order to catch a glimpse of British life in the raw.

Mrs Cripplestone's boarding-house is one of those classical dishes of creamy stucco to which the architects saw fit to add a chunk of Parthenon icing. Under the neo-Grecian entrance, to which you attain by climbing three steps that are religiously whitened every Monday, is a small brass knocker, glinting at you like a beady eye out of the green door. The simplicity of the cream-coloured façade with its sash windows leaves you unprepared for the maze of dark passages within—a characteristic of so many London dwellings which, unable to grow in height, have expanded laterally into their neighbours. The result is a labyrinth of different floor levels, winding corridors and surprise staircases such as you get in the Navy. In my room, where the floor sloped gently, the inkpot on the desk had a habit of moving under its own steam along a pre-established course at a speed varying with the weight of the bus and truck traffic outside. I had greater trouble getting used to the north-east by south-east drift of the bed, and waking up in the middle of the room after dropping off to sleep next to the wall was a disconcerting experience.

Mrs Cripplestone, who has commanded this land ship for the last thirty-five years, seems to be hewn of the same stout timber. Constructed in 1879, added to from 1893 to 1897 thanks to the exertions of the headmistress of Godolphin College,[1] Mrs Cripplestone was entrusted to the proprietary care of a first mate, Ramsay Dunbar, who died prematurely after losing his fortune between Epsom and Newmarket, and then had the finishing touches put to her by a colonel of the Indian Army, W. R. S. Cripplestone, who preserved himself in whisky to a ripe old age.

The two deceased spouses are still hanging—one around Mrs Cripplestone's neck, the other on her bosom, in two medallions of wrought silver, and the fact that she cannot make a move without putting the colonel through his paces in the full dress uniform of the Bengal Lancers confers on her a singular author- ity. Her lofty stature, the haughty mien of a sallow countenance whose noble jowls contrast with a battleaxe nose, the souvenirs of close to a century sprinkled over her blouse of Nottingham lace, her long neck held upright by a black ribbon behind which her Adam's apple seems to play a game of hide and seek, and her lengthy, severe, purple skirts make Mrs Cripplestone one of the most authentic monuments of the Victorian age. (Visiting hours: Tuesdays and Thursdays 4 to 6.) Also her practice of boring through you with a steely eye from behind her lorgnette in Seychelles (G.B.) tortoiseshell contributes in no small degree towards maintaining a strictly Spartan discipline in the house- hold.

Here the old customs are still respected. Every morning at seven o'clock, whether you like it or not, an Irish dragon by the name of Jennifer bursts into your room in her vegetable green

[1] Miss Eleanor Savernake, famed for having developed a form of *proper deport- ment* exercise intended to straighten the spines of young girls by having them stand motionless for an hour with a glass of water on their heads. She thus added an inch and a half to the Duchess of Ratigan and an inch to Mrs Cripplestone.

AFTER THE EXPLOSION: HOUR OF RECKONING AT MRS CRIPPLESTONE'S

serge dress and her white linen cap to bring you—in the solemn name of the British Empire—the first cup of 'early morning tea' which ushers in the English day. Duly answering this matutinal bugle call, the four widows, seven spinsters and three retired army majors who make up Mrs Cripplestone's permanent guests then harness themselves for the second cup of tea, the real one, which is served downstairs in the dining-room, where amid tables and sideboards of genuine mahogany four Indian elephants' feet are stolidly ending their careers as aspidistra pots.

At the detonation caused by the explosion of the water-heater, I was immediately confronted by this entire, respectable company. With my pyjamas three-quarters burned off by the explosion, my hair dishevelled, my face blackened, and my body hastily covered by a flannel towel serving as a loincloth, I had to face these already fully dressed people. Mrs Cripplestone, after examining me for a moment through her lorgnette, quickly averted her gaze from the hideous and disgusting spectacle I presented.

'Really!' she said, without looking at me. 'I don't see how you ever managed such a thing! Mrs Peacock'—who was standing right behind her not missing a trick—'has been taking two baths a week here ever since 1920, and I have not once had a disturbance of this sort with her. Really, it's quite shocking!'

Shocking, indeed! Mrs Cripplestone, it turned out, was uneasy about sending me the plumber's bill, and I soon gathered without her having to rub it in that it might be pretty steep. What plagued me, however, was not the prospect of paying, nor even the ridiculous attire in which Mrs Cripplestone had caught me and which had revealed the very first day to her lady clients a secret that many of them might otherwise never have discovered. It was an unbearable guilt complex which overwhelmed me every time I opened the dining-room door and heard people whispering back and forth in a great rustling of sibilants: 'Look, it's the Frenchman who blew up the geyser!'

The next few days I was allowed to use the bathroom on the third floor, provided that Jennifer put the machine into operation. But once you have got off on the wrong foot with people, it's difficult to regain your aplomb. Two days after the cata-strophe, an unfortunate flick of my bath-towel brought the pink shade of the ceiling light (Regency Period) crashing down on my head.

Unable to stand it any longer, I left Mrs Cripplestone's boarding-house the very next day.

THE LAND OF HIDE AND SEEK

 In the United Kingdom everything seems designed to put the invader off the track, in time of peace as much as in time of war. The camouflaging of street names and house numbers is, of course, a classic weapon employed by General Staffs the world over to disorient enemy parachutists. But the English have adapted it to peacetime purposes with an uncompromising rigour.

For any foreigner with a merely average memory it is next to impossible to keep engraved on it the full address of an Englishman living in the country. He may well succeed in retaining a part of—

> Major W. Marmaduke Thompson
> The Tower
> Rough Hill Road
> Marlborough Heights
> Ploughbury
> Hampshire

but, considering that none of this is pronounced as it is written, is it surprising that the visitor ends up by mislaying a good half of it?

The first thing I learned, on reaching Ploughbury, was that Ploughbury was not there, but a little farther on at a place called Fortescue. Coming to some heights—those of Marlborough as I ascertained from a passer-by—I was lucky enough to run into a nameless lane which, I was courteously informed, was Rough Hill Road. This lane was bordered on each side by some fifty brick bungalows indistinguishable from one another save by the floral decoration in front of them.

In most countries, when they finish a house, architects move on a little farther and build another that is different. But in England, when they've finished one house, without wasting an inch of space, they promptly stick an identical one right next to it—with the same bricks, the same bay window, the same little garden, the same doorway and the same furniture. In fact, only when he sees his wife's face—and even then assuming he hasn't stopped at the local on the way—can an Englishman be sure he's really home.

Even then he can be none too sure. . . . For it's a funny thing, the similarity in their houses seems to have engendered an isomorphism in their inmates. When the Good Lord—time and weather permitting—lets His eye roam over England at 8 a.m., He must see the same man (multiplied by twenty million) leaving the same house via the same garden after conferring the same tender look on the lawn-mower and the same absent-minded kiss on the (left) cheek of the same wife who, having waved him goodbye with her (right) hand, walks back through the same bay-windowed living-room, where the same wild ducks pursue their V-shaped flight in the same painting of Peter Scott's 'Sunset on the River', after which she goes upstairs to make herself up in the same bedroom in front of the same dressing-table, graced with the same three ornaments—an oval mirror, a brace of hair-curlers, and a perfume bottle marked 'Evening in Paris'.

On Rough Hill Road I noticed that certain houses bore names and others numbers—never the two at once—and that some had neither.

I asked an inhabitant who was busy gardening if he knew Major Thomspon's house.

'You mean The Castle?'

'No, The Tower.'

'Yes, that's it!'

And thus it was that I ran the Major to earth in The Tower, which was really The Castle, in the township of Ploughbury, which was really Fortescue. It was all pretty far from Rough Hill Road, which I had long left far behind me without ever getting away from it. With its tall brick chimneys, its ivy-covered façade, and its small-paned, lancet windows, the Major's manor house, without being exactly lordly, bore an unmistakable Tudor stamp. Defying the brisk wind blowing over Marlborough Heights, the Major himself was gardening in grey flannels and a striped blazer, his head bare and a pipe in his mouth. From his face it was clear that this was one of his good days, but the same could not be said for his wife Martine, whose head, thrust out of a second-storey window, seemed to have been half guillotined.[1]

Having more or less disengaged herself, Martine launched into a tirade against this system of ventilation.

'Ah! It's a good thing we are only going to be here for a month or two! With these hunting trophies all over the place, I keep hitting my head on an elephant tusk or the jaw of a tiger! Never, never shall I get used to living in this menagerie!'

Whereupon I saw the stuffed head of a black panther sail through the air and land at the feet of the gardening Major, who, upon examination, simply observed:

'Sumatra . . . 1932.'

After which, Major Thompson resumed planting his Glorious gladiolas, alternating a yellow Nelson with a red Marshal Montgomery, in accordance with the advice proffered on the front of *The Times* by Messrs. Cuthbert and Co., *the Nation's Nurserymen* since 1797.[2]

Visibly exasperated by Marmaduke's phlegmatic calm, Martine burst out of the house and unleashed a broadside against the discomforts of the ancestral mansion.

[1] The French, who first conceived the idea of making doors into windows, have always been baffled by the latter. Their helplessness, in the face of as harmless a household object as a sash window, is attested by the title they have conferred on it in their language—*fenêtre à guillotine*. That the French should never have succeeded in taming this utilitarian device is another proof of the basic superiority of British civilization. The sash window is a typically Anglo-Saxon invention, offering, as it does, a humane compromise between the windy iciness of the out-of-doors and the stifling airlessness of the indoors. (W. M. T.)

[2] The English language is, no doubt, the only one in the world where the word 'nursery' is used to designate both the place where children are brought up and where petunias are grown.

'Don't talk to me,' she exclaimed, 'about this famous British comfort! It's definitely overrated, I say. . . . First I'm frozen to death, and then——'

'That's because you're not properly trained for it, my dear,' Major Thompson interrupted. 'We British are inured to the cold from youth up. At Rugby I had to break the ice in my bath with a hammer, and I jolly well hope those young rascals are still doing it today.[1] Here in England we grow strong because we are taught to endure the cold, and later on we endure the cold because we are strong.'

'You are speaking nonsense, *mon Marminet*,' said Martine in a softer tone. 'You English are more often in bed with your flu than we French are with our *grippe*. Everybody knows that there is only a feefty-feefty chance to have an Englishman keep a rendezvous in winter—not because he is unreliable, but because half of England is in bed.'

'Rubbish!' spluttered the Major.

'Come now! Not only are you always catching colds, but it's hardly possible to wash in your freezing bathrooms. When I think of the scene you made at Châteauroux, because there the basin leaked a bit! It's so typical! You curse the plumbing in Châteauroux but you don't mind to break the ice in Salisbury— provided it is done in the best Tudor style!'

'Preposterous!' exploded the Major. 'At any rate, *we* wash—

---

[1] I can vouch for the accuracy of the Major's statement on this point. I have visited a number of British public schools where it is still as cold as ever. You might almost say that England makes a cult of privation and discomfort. For two thousand years the British have spent their time freezing themselves and they have made of the cold one of their three score and ten religions. Not so long ago two students from Reading spent three nights shivering in a cave on the outskirts of the town, clad only in animal skins and potato sacks—for the simple pleasure of proving that one can live today as men did in prehistoric times. They failed, naturally, to start a fire by rubbing two sticks together and they were reduced to using matches. But apart from that their experiment was an unqualified success. They emerged from their cave in Whiteknights Park more dead than alive, but delighted. It all goes to show once again how much the English love to freeze themselves and to walk around coatless or wearing a simple trenchcoat when the thermometer registers 5 above—just to prove that they are undaunted by the elements. So too in certain London clubs the temperature is never supposed— even in the dead of winter—to rise above 45 degrees.

and more often than certain coddled people who must always have hot water! The best proof of how seldom the French wash is that they look so much cleaner on Sundays!'

'But on that day you wash even less! Ah, you British and your *esprit de contradiction.*[1] . . . Yes, and what about your country houses? They're ice-boxes where the coldest room of all is the one where one undresses completely—the bathroom. . . . And when I think of those awful bedclothes that keep you awake with cold feet. *J'ai horreur de ça!*'

'Martine, dear, you French like your comfort in bed. We like ours seated. I'm never less at ease than on one of your wretched *salons* in a stiff Louis Seize or Directoire chair that seems more anxious to throw me out than to take me in. In France, to talk comfortably you have to go to bed.'

'*Ma Marmine.* . . . Always that old-fashioned notion about the bed-loving Frenchman!'

'Well, Katherine Mansfield herself used to say so, and remember, dear, she wasn't English, she was a New Zealander. Anyway, in our homes there's always a cosy corner where you can relax comfortably in a deep armchair which doesn't make you want to get up and take to your bed.'

'Yes, and it's why your wives get so horribly bored while you snooze in your dreary clubs under cover of *The Times* pretending to be reading about Colonial Office policy in upper Ubanga——'

'Uganda!' the Major corrected.

'Ubanga . . . Uganda . . . or whatever it is! But I am not going to moulder away in this draughty hole much longer. . . . Besides, we must go up to London, if only to take out the Pochets! All we have done for them so far was to see them to their hotel——'

There are times when fading away is the better part of discretion. I decided that there was too much electricity in the air to stay on at the Major's. The presence of a guest, with Martine in such a frame of mind, could hardly have cooled the atmosphere.

[1] The reference is to our alleged 'spirit of contradiction' and love of argument. (W. T. M.)

So I used the excuse of an appointment with the Pochets to cut short my visit.

'All the same,' I said to Marmaduke, as I took leave of him, 'why do you insist on hiding the names of your roads and the numbers of your houses, all so diabolically similar, so that one can never tell where one is?'

'Why do you need to know, my dear fellow? Either you live there and you know it. Or you don't live there and don't need to know it. In that way we live in peace—except, of course, when chaps like you come along.'

It is only fair to remark that things are like this only in the country. In London they are far more complicated. There almost every house, though identical with its neighbours, has a number that is out of series.

From the first I lost a lot of precious time searching for Mrs Cripplestone's most Victorian establishment in Cavendish Lane because I stupidly thought of looking for No. 58 between Nos. 56 and 60.

'I'd 'ave a look over 'ere, if I were you,' a delivery boy advised me, leading me over to the house next to No. 37.

It sometimes happens, of course, that a number is in its proper place, but after a time in London you get so used to not finding it there you stop looking for it. As a general rule the numbers don't follow on. That would be too monotonous. On one side of the street they go in ascending order, on the other side in descending order. Sometimes they stop descending, in order to ascend, only to pause exhausted, and resume their descent.

From Tacitus to Diderot and Nietzsche, every writer of note has stressed the fact that the English are melancholic, morose and gloomy people. Fertile soil indeed for the cultivation of humour —that gay plant watered by sadness! Even when the English laugh, they keep it well concealed. Where do they keep their sense of fun? At least in part, in the numbering of their houses. A race of master humorists, the English have managed a miracle —the miracle of 'property' humour. In France a tourist often has the impression that people are laughing at him inside their houses behind the shutters. But in England, where there are no shutters, it is the houses themselves that mock you.

Even the streets are capricious in the extreme. Relax your attention for a moment and you will find that they have changed their name or lost it completely. Sometimes they lose it for a minute or two, assume another, and then, after due reflection, readopt the first. Delightful fantasy!

It can also happen that a main street keeps its surname on the right, after changing its patronymic on the left. It was thus that Pochet got himself ticked off by his wife for arriving three hours late at 55 Prince's Gate, which they had forgotten to inform him was to be found in Exhibition Road. Not only does it bore English streets to have the same name all the time, but they dislike keeping to just one part of the town. It's the sportive side of English topography which, by its glorious uncertainty, obeys one of the United Kingdom's basic laws: always give chance and the weaker fellow his innings. This is a law as applicable to things as to individuals and animals, and it is as binding for the fox, which it would be an outrage to shoot, as for Napoleon, whom it would have been unsporting to remove to St Helena without promptly founding a secret society dedicated to his rescue.[1]

It is, after all, only fair play that the rolling English road should upset the calculations of the mile-hungry motorist by interposing hedgerows and unexpected roundabouts. If there weren't twenty-three High Streets, thirteen King Streets and eleven Duke Streets in London, what merit would there be in finally running one of them down?

Besides, one must grant the English this: they are very kind. When they see you are lost, they don't hesitate to accompany

[1] Little known in France, this society had many adherents in Great Britain where Napoleon's gaoler, Hudson Lowe, has never enjoyed a good press, whereas the Emperor remains extremely popular. In a poll conducted among twelve-year-old students at a London school by a Professor Frank Dash, it was found that in answer to the question: 'Whom do you admire the most?' Napoleon figured at the head of the list with Field-Marshal Montgomery, and ahead of Nelson, Churchill and William the Conqueror.

you right up to the point where they get lost with you. Whereupon they entrust you to the care of another helpful citizen or of
a 'Bobby' who generally gets you to take the Tube or directs you
in an utterly incomprehensible fashion.

Not long after my invasion of The Tower, Pochet and I set
out in search of Shrewsbury Place, the site of the residence of
Colonel Basil Cranborne, an old friend of Marmaduke. Pochet
approached one of those impressive 'Bobbies' who can't help
looking down at you in the most disconcerting way. Having
received the desired directions on his nose, so to speak, Pochet
came back towards me with dismay written all over his
face.

'I'm no better off than I was before. No wonder these people
don't have the same appetite as we. Between meals they eat half
their words. And they've got 450,000 of them.[1] I didn't catch
a word of what that giant said to me, except of course, "You
can't miss it!" I occasionally get lost on my own, but when an
Englishman says to me, "You can't miss it," I'm bound to go
wrong.'

Even the English get lost in their labyrinths, and how could it
be otherwise?

As we were looking for Shrewsbury Place and had finally
turned into Shrewsbury Avenue, we could expect at any moment to run the place down. But in England a Place is anything
but a place. A Place is a square. A Square, however, can be a
close. And a Close, as often as not, can be a short street. One
thing does at any rate simplify matters—you can be sure that a
Terrace is never a terrace. It is just another street. So why rack
your brains over it? You have to be afflicted with the wretched
logic of a Continental to insist on finding a garden where the
address reads Gardens or a gate when it reads Gate. And when
you think that there are sixty-five different words for a street in
England, why on earth should they simply call it a street? It's
much jollier to call it a mews or a crescent.

[1] To be exact, 455,000 words in the *Oxford English Dictionary*, as against
70,000 words in the *Grand Larousse* and 40,000 in the *Dictionnaire de l'Académie*.

'Well,' groaned Pochet, exhausted, 'what would you say to a drink?'

We were lucky enough to run down a pub that was still open.[1] But hardly had we ordered a couple of whiskies than we were asked to gulp them down immediately:

'You've just three more minutes to finish your drinks,' the gentleman bottle-washer informed us.

At this announcement a good score of customers rushed across the street to another pub just opposite ours, which closed half an hour later. Each side of the street belonged, we discovered, to a different borough, so that not only the hours of closing but even the street lighting was different. The pavement on our side was lit by gaslight, and on the other side by electricity.

'Can I take a bottle of whisky with me?' Pochet inquired.

'Read the Licensing Regulations!' he was told.

The licensing rules read as follows:

1. Consumers may not take any form of spirits with them outside the hours of lawful consumption.
2. Any order given during lawful opening hours may be delivered at home outside of the lawful hours.
3. Any order made from outside during the closing hours may be delivered at home outside of closing hours if a period of opening hours has occurred in the interim.[2]

'All right,' said Pochet, 'give me some aspirin instead.'

It wasn't a joke. Pochet had indeed acquired a headache. Leaving the pub, he stepped in at a chemist's to buy some aspirin, and while he was about it some toothpaste. The pharmacist agreed to sell him the aspirin, but as for the toothpaste, which he had right next to him, the legal hour was up . . . Pochet thus

[1] The public houses in London are allowed to serve liquors at varying times, depending on the part of the town.
[2] From this it can be deduced—more or less clearly—that while you cannot take a bottle of whisky out once the pub has closed its doors, you can have the bottle follow you if you can get someone to bring it to your domicile.

learned that in the United Kingdom there is an hour for head-
aches and another for brushing one's teeth.

'*Mon Dieu!*' he sighed. 'What a country!'

It was late indeed when we finally found Colonel Basil Cranborne's house. The visiting card I had with me indicated the
'ground floor', so I rang the doorbell on the street level. An
elderly lady came to open the door.

'Colonel Cranborne?'

'Upstairs.'

'But isn't this the ground floor?'

'No, it's the basement.'

'And the ground floor?'

'Up the steps. I think you'll find it's inhabited,' added the
old lady.

I gathered from this odd dialogue that in some London
houses, if you are told that the ground floor is inhabited, it means
that there are people on the *first* floor.

A good bit of this confusion could no doubt be avoided if we
could only reach some kind of *entente* on words. But here again
the English do their damnedest to mystify the foreigner. Not
only have the English borrowed some 32,500 words from
abroad—and never bothered to return them—but to those they
have kept they have given a completely new twist. Once a
French term has been confiscated by the English language it
acquires a meaning quite different from—if not completely opposite to—that which you expect. And if, out of friendship,
the French borrow a few English words to enrich their own
vocabulary, the English promptly assert that such words no
longer mean anything to them—like *footing*, for example.[1]
How can one ever understand a people who use the word *grand*,

---

[1] '*Faire du footing*' is a French expression that means taking brisk walks. But let
us forget all this tall talk about French generosity and English rapacity and ask
ourselves in all seriousness what one is to think of a people who call a thousand
million a *billion* and a billion a *trillion*, an umbrella a *parapluie* and a parasol an
ombrelle, a cap a *casquette* and a casket a *coffret*, a chat a *causerie* and a cat a *chat*,
a parrot a *perroquet* and a parakeet a *perruche*, who call a magpie a *pie*, a pie a *tarte*,
and a tart a *grue*? (W. M. T.)

but don't mean something big, who say a *merchantman* when they mean a cargo vessel, and a *vessel* when they mean a jug, who use the word *habit* not to designate a costume, but a custom, who insist on using a yard that contains 914 millimetres, a pound that equals 450 grammes at one moment and 480 the next, a ton that oscillates between 1016 and 907 kilogrammes, and an ounce which has one value for the pharmacist and another for the grocer? All of this is part of that elaborate camouflage intended to hamstring the foreigner with such diabolic inventions as cricket, the secret aim of which is to be so obscure that it will give any alien attempting to understand it a headache and drive him to drink once he thinks he has unravelled its secrets.

'When I think,' Madame Pochet exclaimed to me, 'of the trouble I had finding out that a pound contains twenty shillings, a shilling twelve pence, and a half-crown two shillings and six pence! And all to what purpose? So that I could walk into a shop to buy a Cashmere cardigan and have the price thrown at me in guineas, that is in a form of currency that hasn't existed for a hundred and thirty-eight years, but which is still worth slightly more than a pound. *Ah, non! Quel casse-tête!*' [1]

---

[1] Literally 'What a head-break!' A colloquial French expression commonly used when the French finally give up and admit they can't explain us. (W. M. T.)

THE PURSUIT OF PRECEDENT

(or 'The Strange Case of the Intrusive Egg')

ONE of the marked superiorities the English enjoy over other peoples is their ability to imbue the foreigner with a crippling inferiority complex the moment he sets foot on British soil—indeed, even before he gets a chance to do so.

The Pochets were overjoyed at the prospect of being able to make their entry into Great Britain with Major Thompson. But this entry was made through two quite different doors. The Major, as a British subject, was already freely treading the soil of Albion while they, as 'aliens', were being finely screened.

Now this word 'alien' has a singularly exasperating effect on Madame Pochet.

'*Tout de même*, we're not lepers, are we? When one thinks that these people call themselves the most civilized in the world! You could perfectly well get here by the underground, but no! The English force you to get sea-sick or air-sick before ever getting here—and all on account of a mere puddle of water that would hardly stretch from Paris to Versailles! And the result? You get here deflated.'

She had barely uttered these words when Her Majesty's Customs officials confiscated her white poodle, Virgule, because, as a continental dog, she could only enter the United Kingdom after a six months' quarantine. As everyone knows, ever since 1885 (cf. Pasteur) French dogs have been mad. And as Virgule, unnerved by the commotion, forgot herself on the red base of a Royal Mail box, the Customs man added:

"We'll teach her to behave herself properly. . . .' [1]

The leave-taking from Virgule, accomplished under the impassive stare of the British immigration officers, was a heart-rending spectacle. Madame Pochet was all ready to re-embark.

'You might at least have warned me, Major,' she said to Marmaduke.

'I thought you knew,' said the Major who, on hearing Madame Pochet's cries of distress, had made a momentary sortie from the United Kingdom and an unexpected *entrée* into the no-man's-land of *aliens*.

Madame Pochet made one final attempt to circumvent the Cerberus of Customs officialdom.

'I demand you, please——' she began.

The immigration officer took the request very badly.

'I demand means *j'exige*,' the Major explained. 'Hardly ever used here. Say "I ask".'

'*Je n'askerai rien*,' said Madame Pochet. 'That's just too much!'

While Madame Pochet was thus being deprived of Virgule, Pochet was having troubles of his own with the police. The first question an 'alien' is asked on entering the United Kingdom is: 'How long are you going to stay?' Which is tantamount to asking: 'When are you thinking of leaving?' The second question is: 'What are you coming over here to do?' Two questions that are enough to unsettle the most innocent soul. One of Her Majesty's immigration officers has only to ask me what I have come to England for, and I no longer know myself. The most inoffensive visit thus immediately assumes an alarming character to Scotland Yard. But it is just as dangerous to try to browbeat your way through by answering, as did that inveterate joker, Pochet:

'If anyone asks you, *mon ami*, just tell them you don't know.'

---

[1] The English claim that their dogs, disciplined from the tenderest age, are better brought up than other dogs. There must be something in the English air which makes the dogs there behave more properly than on the continent. Perhaps it's the way their owners have of addressing them like gentlemen, by saying, for example: 'Will you kindly leave the room, Master Dick!'

Whereupon he burst into a hearty laugh which the stiff-faced official opposite him did not seem to appreciate. Pochet was forthwith handed a list of articles banned by Her Majesty's Customs, where, beneath the emblem of the Lion and the Unicorn, a solemn interdiction was placed on the importation of parrots, musk-rat and leg of mutton (unless pre-cooked on the continent).

This childish fear of not-to-be-committed crimes overwhelms the foreigner the moment he sets foot on British soil and it does not relinquish him until he has left the country. There is—at any rate for the Continental—something almost adulterous in this sense of insecurity. You have only to be the married man hastening to a secret assignation to find your route encumbered with placid strollers, child in hand, or with citizens with limpid consciences, never straying from the beaten path that leads from home to office and whose unclouded gaze seems to lay bare the sinner's lust for debauch. Here fifty-three million citizen policemen[1] look with a disapproving eye at the agile Latin who moves up ten places in the queue, thereby breaking that fundamental rule which the English would never think of circumventing. The Rule! And, stricter than any code engraved in marble, that unwritten law, the law of phantoms: tradition—which, with anthracite, is Great Britain's most precious raw material.

Wherever you may walk, or stop, or breathe in England you can feel the weight of a thousand years of history bearing down on you—the maximum of historical density being concentrated in the Tower of London, with its walls sweating the blood of princes, and that grim dungeon where Edward IV had his brother drowned in a butt of Malmsey.

The English love to make telephone calls in eighteenth-century sedan chairs, to sip tomato juice in an inn founded in

[1] Little more than a century ago the English acted as their own police. This habit is as evident in their sense of discipline as in their affection for the 'Bobbies', the only policemen in the world who are not armed. (They owe their appellation to the first name of their creator, Sir Robert Peel.)

1135, to sit down at a sixteenth-century table to savour Elizabethan cucumbers and to have pointed out to them in Gothic lettering the way to the

𝕷𝖆𝖛𝖆𝖙𝖔𝖗𝖞

One day, when I was in Haymarket, I walked into a tobacconist's and asked for some tobacco. Instantly I knew I had made a mistake. You just don't walk into Fribourg and Treyer, Tobacconists, Established in 1720, and ask for tobacco, as you would on the Champs-Élysées. The gentleman behind the counter couldn't have been more shocked if I had asked him for a waffle. Tobacco? Of course, but what kind of tobacco?

'If you want to,' Major Thompson—who was with me—whispered into my ear, 'you can ask for Waterloo Mixture or Wingate Mixture, or for any other of the many blends that Fribourg and Treyer have handed down from father to son and inscribed in their books for their customers since 1720. You can, like Beau Brummel, Mrs Siddons, or Disraeli, order a mixture of Masulipatam and Latakia, but for the love of God, don't just ask for tobacco! . . . Do I call the *sommelier* at the Tour d'Argent and ask him for red wine? Why not try my favourite mixture—as a matter of fact, it's William Pitt's.'

Even when the Major smokes, it's a puff of history that he blows out of his pipe.

As we were not too far from St James's Street and Pochet wanted to buy a hat, we made for Lock's venerable shop (established 1759), in the window of which are exhibited, like the flags of the Invalides in Paris, glorious, threadbare trophies of the past (such as the nineteenth century's first bowler hat).

Pochet had his hand on the doorknob, when the Major said to him: 'Nelson, my dear Pochet, used to open this very same door.'

An evocation like this, when you are about to enter a hat-shop, is enough to turn the soberest head. Later Pochet confided to me that he had felt his soft grey hat literally wilt with humility over his ears. After pausing for a moment inside to examine a bill (carefully kept under glass) which His Grace the Duke of Bedford had settled in 1760, Pochet submitted his cranium to the mercies of a solemn-faced salesman who gazed with dismay at the strange and foreign thing the visitor was wearing on his head.

'I would like to buy a bowler hat,' Pochet announced.

'We don't sell bowlers, sir,' the vendor answered. 'We fit them.'

The salesman disappeared, then returned and thrust down on Pochet's startled brow the still warm form of a bowler hat, which in a few seconds turned as hard as wood. Five minutes later and for the first time in his life, Pochet walked out with a date—1759—on his head.

The English do not simply have a passion for the old. One of their favourite sport is the hunt for precedents.[1] Whenever something new occurs in England, the first concern of its inhabitants is to determine if such a thing has ever happened before. Suppose, for example, that the Arsenal football team scores three goals in four minutes. Two thousand five hundred sports writers will immediately finger feverishly through dust-covered almanacs in pursuit of a precedent. Now suppose you stop your car in the middle of Westminster Bridge at midday. No doubt you will have some words with the police. However, if you can furnish proof that by virtue of a privilege of the Crown your ancestor, the Earl of Sherborne, was entitled in 1496 to halt his carriage in the middle of the bridge, you stand a good chance of winning your case.[2]

[1] Nothing could better attest the real affection lavished by the English on all that is old than the example of a friend of Marmaduke's, a certain Dr Robinson, whom I went to consult. On each visit I was startled to see a 1925 Rolls-Royce with carefully polished chrome-plating stationed in front of his door. I asked him if he knew the owner of this immobile vehicle. 'I am the owner,' he told me. 'Don't you want to turn it in for a more recent model?' I asked. 'Actually,' he answered, 'the car I use is in a garage behind the house. This one doesn't go but it impresses my patients.'

[2] A Professor of International Law once provoked an uproar at the University of London by presenting a thesis in French. When his colleagues objected that

Whereas the new upsets the British, precedents reassure them. They track down old dates as we do rabbits. At heart they dislike doing anything that hasn't been done at least once since 1066. Perhaps this explains why so many English women die old maids.

While the French, armed with their Littrés and their Larousses, wage strenuous verbal battles to determine whether one should say *le Normandie, la Normandie,* or simply *Normandie,* the English, who are less given to going into action on behalf of syntax, carry on mighty battles of dates.

The Times is a particularly choice arena for such jousts. Not long ago a correspondent wrote to the editor of this venerable daily to call his attention to the unwonted presence of a fried egg in the mixed grill served to him by a West End restaurant. Never, to his knowledge, had such an incongruity been perpetrated before. But an Englishman should know that one should never say 'never'. For several days later *The Times* published a letter citing the presence of such an egg in a mixed grill as early as 1922 in Cambridge. This was the signal for an immense movement of opinion. For weeks five hundred thousand Englishmen were passionately aroused by the column in *The Times* entitled 'The Intrusive Egg'. One of them seems to

---

this was contrary to the established usage, he replied that he had based his action on a decree dating from 1116. Everyone was delighted.

It took the English a century and a half to realize that the Grenadier Guard stationed in front of No. 10 Downing Street 167 years earlier, after an attempt on Walpole's life, was no longer needed.

English justice itself is founded on precedents. There is no written code of law, but only collections of precedents which the Justices refer to. When no precedent exists, one is created, after much ado. One of the most recent and typical cases was that involving William Joyce, who was brought to trial for treason for having made wartime broadcasts for the Nazi radio under the name of Lord Haw-Haw. Not being British either by birth or by adoption, Joyce did not—according to his defence counsel—owe allegiance to the Crown. The prosecution argued that he did, since he was the holder of a British passport. The question was thus to determine whether the holder of a British passport becomes by the same token British. No one could answer the question, for precedents were looked for in vain. After a long session, Mr Justice Tucker made legal history by deciding that Joyce owed obedience to the Crown by virtue of his passport. Today this is part of the common law. Joyce was hanged.

have had the last word with a poached egg spotted by a shocked Englishman's eyes in a mixed grill in Dublin in 1918.[1]

[1] Though I too, succumbing to the fever of research, succeeded in unearthing a reference to a similar egg among the parchments of one of my ancestors—a contemporary of the Black Prince—*The Times* was unwilling to accept this case as a valid precedent, the mixed grill not having been an established culinary feature at the time of the Hundred Years War. Too bad! But how, in the face of such an astonishing display of interest, can anyone seriously claim that the British aren't interested in the art of cooking? But this is a subject about which I have some things of my own to say, and which, to the detriment of Pochet and with the permission of Daninos, I shall need more than a footnote to expound. (W. M. T.)

WITH POCHET IN BRITAIN

WHENEVER I travel with Pochet there are always more than two of us—a phenomenon which, for an Englishman at any rate, is not a little disconcerting. Pochet is never alone when he leaves his native France; a ghost accompanies him. His is not a spirit akin to our noble phantoms of Scotland and Cornwall; it is a less aristocratic one in the shape of beefsteak and chips. It is, none the less, an obsessive ghost, not to say a devouring one.

A couple of hours cannot go by in London, or indeed, elsewhere, without Pochet's suddenly feeling himself haunted by this ghost, which reduces him to a state of piteous servitude.

'Ah, I'd give anything for a *bon bifteck* and *pommes frites*,' he says, adding a moment afterwards, 'You know, a really good one, *comme on le fait chez nous*'.[1]

Pochet is the living proof of the extent to which the Frenchman is the slave of his stomach, to say nothing of his liver, an organ he never stops talking about, but which we British have never admitted to polite society. There is indeed no stranger spectacle imaginable than that of Pochet wandering through the streets of Piccadilly in the desperate search for a Chateaubriant or even, incredible as it may sound, of a *guignolet-kirsch*.[2] It's no earthly use my telling him that when it comes to steak, we can hold our own.

'You lent us the word, I'll grant you,' he says, 'but it's we who make the dish.'

Heavens! If only he would make some effort to adapt himself to foreign cooking without, of course, attaining our degree of

---

[1] 'as we do it at home.'
[2] A form of French aperitive, made from a cherry base.

ease, since everywhere abroad we are certain of eating better than at home—things would go more smoothly. But Pochet is convinced that France is the only place where people know how to eat. That's all there is to it. I must say, though, that things are not always made easy for him. The other day in a West End restaurant he was baffled by a menu which gave him a choice between two *plats du jour*—Lancashire hot pot and Irish stew. So he asked the advice of the waitress, one of those blue-faced matrons, in a mauve uniform and a white serving cap, who smack more of the hospital nurse than of the *haute cuisine*.

'What would you advise me to take?' asked Pochet in his jolly way, 'Lancashire hotpot or Irish stew?'

'I am sorry, sir, we aren't here to give advice, only to serve,' the waitress replied.

Somewhat put off, Pochet plumped arbitrarily for the Lancashire hot pot which, if I may say so, went down badly with his French digestive system. He then declared to me in a sour mood that in France the waiter would have been delighted by such a question and would immediately have unfolded his own *petite idée* as to what was good and what was not. After which he went on to complain that people who devour kippered herring and kidneys when they get up in the morning cannot possibly furnish any useful advice as to what to eat at lunch time; that we British are quite content to naturalize in boiling water all that we get from abroad—everything from our famous 'roast beef of old England' (which we get from the Argentine) to our Canterbury Lamb (from New Zealand) and our Brussels sprouts, for which we reserve a positively inhuman treatment; and finally that because we don't eat properly at mealtimes, we consume the world's greatest quantity of chocolates and sweets in between.

I never reply to insults, especially when they are justified. My country's cooking is in the image of itself—surrounded by water. That is why I so often take Pochet to London restaurants where French, Italian and Chinese chefs dispense an excellent British cuisine. But even then Pochet is not satisfied. He has only to have something put down on his plate for him to think of something that isn't there. The first question he asked me, when I

'WE AREN'T HERE TO GIVE ADVICE, ONLY TO SERVE!'

took him to an Indian restaurant on Swallow Street to taste the curried lamb of my beloved Punjab, was:

'Do you like the Chinese?'

I was startled by the question and told him that I had nothing in particular against them.

'No,' said Pochet, 'I mean Chinese cooking.'

Whereupon he launched into such a succulent description of a Cantonese rice dish he was in the habit of eating in the rue Erlanger that it completely neutralized the taste of the curry. It occurred to me that he might be happier in a Chinese restaurant in Soho. But hardly had he begun attacking his duck *laqué* than he was off on a mouth-watering evocation of a particular *couscous*[1] he had run down in some place on the rue Montyon.

[1] A North African dish made of semolina and bits of lamb.

With this mania of his for transporting me to North Africa when I want to take him to China, or to China when I want to take him to India, I end up no longer knowing where I am or what I am eating!

I must admit that even when I am in Paris and at his house, I find myself in much the same straits, thanks to that strange game of musical dishes ('Give me some of your white meat and I'll give you a piece of the back') which the French play at the dinner-table and which keeps me from being master of my own chicken. Having helped herself to a drumstick, Madame Pochet is suddenly tempted by some white meat on her husband's plate, while he is busy lifting a bit of his liver over to my plate, saying, 'Have a taste of this, Major!' On one occasion, I recall, I had to sit by and watch half my bacon disappear because *Belle-Maman* [1] wanted a bit of it, only to be recompensed by having Pochet Junior's sweetbreads land in my plate. This habit of sticking your fork into your neighbour's plate to scoop up a morsel or deposit a titbit is unknown in Britain, where we take as little relish in poaching on our neighbour's plate as we do in consuming what is on our own.

That is why, when I'm in France and want to savour some tasty stewed eel, I prefer being alone. For if Pochet is with me, he will immediately start talking about the best stewed eel he ever tasted in his life—'It was in Bordeaux, in '38 . . . no, '37, *chez la mère Musignard* . . .' and my eel will suddenly seem to have lost all its savour.

Yes, Pochet will certainly never get used to England—no more than Martine or my good friend Daninos. More's the pity!

I remember, back in the days of my tender youth—if one can so refer to an English youth more accustomed to being caned than coddled—that once, when I was returning from Italy with my father, he took me up on deck, and pointing towards the pale white cliffs emerging from the fog, he cried:

'Look, my son! The cliffs of Dover! I feel safe at last.'

And he breathed in a deep lungful of bracing British air. He was

[1] 'Mama-in-law.'

happy to have escaped unharmed from the Mediterranean world. He was about to regain the only possible land on earth—England.

Well, it's just the opposite with Martine and Pochet. The moment they set foot in the United Kingdom they recoil. Pochet recently told me so himself in one of those strange confession-monologues to which the French are addicted:

'There's nothing to be done about it, Major! It's no use my walking around with an eighteenth-century date on my hat. My skull just isn't British, and it never will be. I try, like you, to start up a conversation by casually remarking, "Do you think the situation in Tanganyika should be regarded as very serious?" I make repeated efforts to handle my umbrella as you do, to keep my elbows glued to my sides, and to sip my tea like a gentleman, but it's no good. . . . Your countrymen have a way of behaving, and dressing, and speaking, and of not speaking, that is like nobody else's. I suppose that is why I have the ceaseless impression that I am being mercilessly scrutinized by people who think to themselves, "He's not a member of the club!"

'Yes, Major, exclusive though it is, this is an enormous club, a club in which everything is a club, from the public school to the House of Lords, the Navy and the Court, a club of fifty-three million members who, from a hundred different ways of doing things, have chosen the most difficult, and, having trained themselves at it for centuries, can now sit back and watch the foreigner make a fool of himself. Look at the boys at Harrow! It's difficult enough to keep on a straw hat, as they do, by slanting it steeply towards their noses. They could easily hold them on by passing the elastic under their chins; instead, they stretch it round the back of their necks.

'An Englishman can perfectly well walk around with a leek in his buttonhole, and it will hardly be noticed, all the more so in that it might be some custom dating from 1687. The other evening I saw a man in white shorts and a singlet jogging down Bayswater Road at five o'clock in the afternoon. Imagine a Parisian trotting it around the Place de l'Opéra in his shorts on the dot of 6.30! If one thing can be certain, it's that at 6.35 he would be explaining his strange behaviour to the nearest Commissariat de

The Englishman goes to school disguised
as a gentleman of the Stock Exchange . . .

. . . dresses up at the Univer
as a small boy . .

. . . marries in uniform

. . . does his war service (se
as a false sheik . . .

. becomes a Sunday School boy again to go to the Stock Exchange . . .

. . . dons a medieval garb for public functions . . .

es to the House of Lords an ermine cape . . .

. . . but is astonished, when he crosses the Channel, to find other people dressed up for no good reason.

Police. But in Bayswater Road no one even turned around to look at him. Stuck in a traffic jam, those Londoners in their buses and cars paid not the slightest attention to this fellow country-man of theirs who was overtaking them on foot. Some English-man must have started running around London in 1705, so that ever since it has been a normal thing to do.

'I might add,' Pochet went on, warming to his theme, 'that there is not a country in the world where people spend more time disguising themselves. Here everyone seems to be in uni-form—even the civilians. And everybody, at every hour of the day, seems to be carrying out some ritual. In France people can get into uniforms, but the civilian in them still comes out. The man on leave is still discernible beneath the uniform of the soldier. The bus conductor, you feel, is anxious to get rid of his ticket-punch and to be able to potter about again in his shirt-sleeves. The policeman who knocks off his tour of duty at the stroke of seven in the morning, to return to his *pot-au-feu*, has already ceased to be a *sergent de ville*. But here in England the uniform makes the person. It impregnates him, it absorbs him. The Chelsea Pensioner seems never to have worn anything but a black shako and a red tunic, and it's difficult to imagine the Lord Mayor of London doffing his chain to put on his pyjamas. From the small boys in top hats and the students in mortarboards and black gowns to the flowing robes of Sir Winston Churchill, the English never stop dressing up—except, of course, on just those occasions when we French do so. None, therefore, of those black crêpe veils and mourning clothes which here would be taken as signs of ostentation!

'This impression of not being a "member of the family" I felt particularly strongly the other night at that gala evening you got me invited to at His Grace's the Duke of Wuthering (P.C., K.T.) whose title goes back, you say, to the thirteenth century. In ad-dition to a multitude of blue-blooded baronets, there were there the Marquesses—I was about to say of Cholmondeley——'

'Chumley,' I corrected him.

'—Chumley, as you say, with that passion you British have for only leaving half of a word after you have sneezed it out, and

Sal'sbury, which is liquefied when pronounced. But the foreign guests were clustered particularly thickly around the Duke of Somerset, no doubt because he has the advantage of having a name that is pronounced nearly as it is written.

'Lost in this dense forest of genealogical trees, in the midst of all these people who had slid down from branch to branch since 1066, I experienced the unsettling sensation of being a lost soul and the only member of my century present. Besides, you showed me so yourself, *cher Major*, in *Whitaker's Almanac*, where a mere twenty lines separate the former Prince of Wales from his Welsh ancestor Trahaern ap Caradog (1075). So too with the members of your club, who seem ever ready to climb into their own portrait frames and to take their places alongside of the Earl of Derby or the Duke of Westminster, draped in their great black robes. When, at your kind invitation, I penetrated into this mausoleum,[1] I found that to become a member I should have had to make a written affirmation of my support of the Declaration of 1832 in favour of the abolition of the Corn Laws. That these laws had in fact been repealed some one hundred and twenty-three years before was of no importance; what was wanted was my opinion in 1832. It is not given to everyone to reverse the gears of history and to declare one's solidarity with the new tendencies of a hundred years before.

'And so, Major, in the presence of the many-centuried guests of the Duke of Wuthering, I, who had the misfortune to come into the world at the time I was born, felt naked as a worm. An uncomfortable feeling that I experience not only in your drawing-rooms, but also on your highways. The other day, while driving towards Bristol, I was about to overtake a bright red lorry when my eye caught a sign on the back of it:

You are following

WINDHAM AND JOHNSON

Purveyors to Her Majesty

Established 1815

[1] Pochet meant the Reform Club, where I like to bury myself of an evening when in London.

'Obviously, if I had read instead:

PICHONNET

Viandes
(Charente-Maritime)

it would not have had the same effect on me. It was as though Napoleon had suddenly appeared between my front buffer and the lorry's exhaust pipe. Traditionally sown with obstacles, the English road now seemed more treacherous than ever. The memory of Waterloo forced me to retreat. If I had had an accident, just think what a figure I should have cut!

'No, it's no use trying to outspeed people who got off to a head start in 1815.

'But to get back to that *soirée* at the Duke of Wuthering's. All this was something I understood much better as a result of following the conversation that evening. For do you know, *mon cher Major*, what it was that everyone was talking about in soft, velvet tones that cushioned all but the sharpest-edged consonants? They were talking of the weather! In France, we speak of the weather, *bien sûr*, but then we go on to something else. But here you don't go on. You stay with the weather. The particular topic of conversation that evening was the damnable weather there had been at the time of the last coronation. There was one aged lord there who rattled off a list of all his coronations in terms of the weather at each. "For Edward VII it rained the evening before . . ." and so on.

'Before long the great question at issue was whether since Edward the Confessor there had been a wetter coronation. Not for nothing, Major, do your countrymen have a passion for precedents. Your history is so rich that it can always provide them with one. In this case it was finally agreed that none existed. Everyone having finally reached agreement on this point around eleven o'clock, a long silence, woven of venerable traditions and affinities, descended upon the drawing-room. The conversation seemed to have died out once and for all. But someone had the *maladresse* to wish to revive it. It was my wife, Solange, who

... THE WETTEST CORONATION SINCE EDWARD THE CONFESSOR'S

thought she was doing the proper thing. There was, as you may imagine, stupefaction on all sides, but it was quickly shattered by the arrival of a dust-covered and panting archer.

'"I return from Agincourt," said the man in the coat of mail. "1415", he added.

'Then he shot off an arrow whose whirring in the air awoke me. For I had finally dozed off to sleep . . . and don't think, Major, that it was because I had not come properly prepared for the occasion. Take this question of the coronation. I had carefully learned by heart the number of diamonds in the Imperial Crown—2783, to be exact—and even the number of silkworms that had spun cocoons for the Queen's robe—52,500. Indeed, I had grown so used to seeing Her Most Gracious Majesty—in magazine photographs—playing with Prince Charles on the age-old lawns of Windsor, or saying good night to Princess Anne, that I had acquired the impression that I was one of the family. So much so that I even began to wonder why I had not yet been invited there. . . .

'But no! I am not ripe for it yet—and I think I never shall be. I should have been more on my guard against people who when learning to speak begin by biting their tongues, and who when eating peas use the backs of their forks as trays on to which they heap little piles with the aid of a knife. I have repeatedly tried to do it, but each Operation *Petits Pois*, like Operation Teacup—which is an exercise in balancing a teacup on your knee—has ended in total defeat. I realized it the other day when lunching with you at Mrs Cripplestone's. Inevitably my *petits pois*—so hard and un-*petit* in England—kept tumbling back on to my plate with a metallic sound. It was no good, *mon cher Major*, your chilling Mrs Cripplestone's blood with a tender account of how the Malays do in their enemies by putting chopped tiger whiskers into their soup, which then harden in the intestines and perforate the peritoneum. Mrs Cripplestone kept one eagle eye on me all the time. And once I had forgotten to pass the port in a clockwise direction, I was a marked man.

'And then there's this question of hands. "*Tes mains, Alfred, tes mains!*" [1] Solange is always saying to me, on the pretext that I gesticulate too much. For my part I don't understand what you English do for gestures; you hardly ever use your hands at all. So here is another enterprise that I must abandon. And all things considered, I wonder if the best way to behave properly in England isn't to go first to Italy, learn to do everything like the Italians, and then do just the opposite.'

[1] 'Your hands, Alfred, your hands!'

CITIZEN-PETS

FOR a long time I used to wonder whether, to get to know the English well, it wouldn't be better to be a zoologist than a psychologist. Today I am convinced of it.

This conviction is one I finally acquired on an English train where, like many other passengers, I was obliged to stand in the corridor because the seats were occupied by dogs. Now if I were to read nonsense like this in a book, I should promptly dash off an angry reader's letter to the author asking if he was trying to make a fool of me. But I can personally guarantee the authenticity of this story, and since even my word of honour may appear insufficient, I shall take the precaution of wrapping it in a piece of the *Daily Telegraph*, that most honourable daily which reported the facts.

The facts are as follows:

On 2nd February 1955, with York as our destination, the Pochets and I boarded the Edinburgh Express, which leaves King's Cross Station in London at 10.35 p.m. The train seemed packed, but when we got on board we discovered that many people were standing in the corridors outside compartments full of dogs but empty of passengers.

After a moment's hesitation and with that deplorable tendency the French have for making a public exhibition of themselves, Madame Pochet decided to invade a compartment, one side of which was serving as a couch for a long-haired greyhound, the other seats being occupied by a pug, two poodles and a fifty-year-old lady who, by one of those tricks of mimicry common among people who spend all their time with animals, had the head of an old mastiff.

'Can you not push this dog over a bit so that I can sit down?' Madame Pochet asked the mastiff-lady.

'Pamela has her ticket, Madame.'

'Of course—but only for *one* seat.'

'No, for the entire side!'

'Still, you are not going to tell me that if I push your animal along a *leetle*—like this. . . .'

The instant Madame Pochet touched the sleek hindquarters of the noble beast with the tip of her umbrella, the mastiff-lady emitted a shrill yelp that rang through the train like an alarm-signal.

'Please stop at once! Don't you know what dog it is you're disturbing? I'm going to complain to the guard.'

Which is precisely what she did.

Madame Pochet thus quickly learned that the beast she had disturbed was none other than Pamela of Quernmore, a Kurdish greyhound and the 'supreme champion' of the United Kingdom. Thus, though the seats were indeed occupied by dogs, they weren't just any old dogs. They were the cream of the dog-world cream, and had been brought down to London from their kennels in Scotland to carry off the most treasured laurels in the canine world—the prizes at the Cruft's Show.

'Don't you know, a dog like that, ma'am,' said the guard, thrusting his chin out in the direction of Pamela of Quernmore, 'is worth a million any day.' And it was quite clear from the glance he then bestowed on Madame Pochet that he valued this foreigner at a far lower figure.

'*Ah! Ça c'est trop fort!*'[1] Madame Pochet exploded. 'Not only do they ask me to stand up in the presence of seated dogs, but then they almost fine me for it! Stay in this *train de chiens* if you want to,' she said turning towards me, 'but I am not staying one second longer. And I am going to complain to the railway company. *Alfred, descendons!*'[2]

---

[1] 'That's too much!'

[2] 'Alfred, let's get out!'

Madame Pochet's complaint, together with those of several other passengers whose love of dogs was not unlimited, was duly registered with the offices of the British Railways, which issued a formal statement of policy a few days later: in general, a dog, even an English dog with his ticket, does not have the right to occupy a railway seat, but in this case the dogs were quite exceptional. The

There was a positively doglike submission in the way Pochet obeyed Madame's injunction. The whole business seemed to have paralysed him. And all my life I shall remember the sight of this man standing mesmerized on the platform as a train full of dogs pulled out before his eyes.

Like my two-legged fellow passengers, I resigned myself to standing for the better part of the night, but, the best places in the corridor being already taken, I was reduced to leaning up against the door to the W.C. in a posture that reminded me of journeys in France during the Occupation.

As I was trying to doze off in this position under the mocking gaze of a cocker spaniel who with his tongue hanging out defied me from the eminence of his corner seat, I wondered if I weren't the victim of an hallucination. I used to imagine that in the infinite diversity of the planets there must exist one on which Man was the noblest conquest of the horse. It had never occurred to me that to find this kind of world it was unnecessary to cross the Milky Way; it was enough to cross the Channel. No, I was not dreaming; that night I was in the Dog Kingdom on Man's earth. The Pochets had indeed got out of this British train and left me to roll on alone towards York. And if at that very moment a St Bernard ticket inspector had suddenly appeared to punch my ticket with his teeth I would not have been surprised.

This strange sensation grew stronger in me when, unable to sleep upright, I pulled out the paper and started to read.

In normal times it is pretty hard to open a British paper without reading something about Welsh miners going on strike in order to get a forty-hour week for their ponies (one and a half columns), or of how one of the Queen's three corgis bit a sentinel at Buckingham Palace who didn't budge a fraction of an inch (two columns and a photo). But this evening the paper beat all records.

British Railways had therefore decided to treat them as gentlemen and had authorized them to occupy passenger seats and even whole compartments. 'The only thing we can reproach certain owners with is their not having put rugs on the seats before setting down their animals,' an official declared.

Whereas only four lines were needed to bury Lord Rupert Featherspin, three entire columns (with photograph) were devoted to the life of Black Knight, the well-known Pekinese, who had just died in 'his country house in Essex at the age of nine years and nine months'. Imagine five lines being devoted to the death of Paul Claudel while the very same day a full half-page is given over to an account of the glorious career of Madame Pochet's poodle—and you'll have some idea of the situation! But here's the point: are there in France dogs like Black Prince? Dogs that sit at the Lord Mayor's table on black satin cushions, eat off the gold plate at the Guildhall, and are made honorary citizens of the City of London? Dogs that attend Queen Elizabeth's wedding in sable coats, have the *entrée* to Buckingham Palace, have their own club, make telephone calls to Naples, profess political opinions, and call upon the Prime Minister at 10 Downing Street? [1]

Obviously not. And under the circumstances it is easy enough to understand how Lady Mimming, Black Knight's companion —one can hardly use the word 'proprietor', for if anyone was possessed in this affair, it was clearly not the dog—could say of him after his death:

'He was the incarnation of a Chinese Emperor and a Ming horse . . . I am inconsolable . . . But I shall send him to the taxidermist and when Black Knight comes back stuffed, he can sleep for ever in his favourite spot—on my bed, his head on his paws.'

---

[1] The members of the Kennel Club in London, which is reserved for owners of eminent hounds, are veritable man-dogs and woman-dogs. They are not addressed by their own names, but by those of their pedigreed beasts. 'Hello, Black!' 'How are you, Husky?' The presentation of new members is likewise made in the name of their dogs.

As for telephone calls to Naples, reference is here made to those which an actress carries on when she is in Capri with Patch, her Queensland Blue Heeler, who receives the communication comfortably seated in his armchair at home. She speaks and Patch barks, her mother holding the receiver for him. 'It cheers me up when I'm feeling blue!' she declared to a group of somewhat startled Neapolitan journalists.

In the same way many Conservatives and Socialists see to it that their dogs have the same political opinions as they themselves. With a little training a Socialist poodle can be made to refuse sugar offered in the name of Churchill, but to accept it in the name of Attlee.

'I KNOW . . . IT'S A BIT AWKWARD, BUT THE GENERAL ASKED IF HE MIGHT
BRING HIS BEST FRIEND ALONG . . .'

In this way I finally fell asleep that night, my fitful slumbers being briefly disturbed every half-hour or so when some bulldog or Great Dane would walk all over me to get to the lavatory. I understood at last the full meaning of the remark made to me by an Italian mason in Arlington Street at the sight of a chauffeur opening the door of a Bentley for a Pekinese in a sealskin: '*Se dovessi vivere ancora una volta, vorrei essere un cane in Inghilterra.*' (If I had to live a second time, I'd be a dog in England.)

Towards one o'clock in the morning I was awakened by a sharp pain in the stomach, and I resumed my reading of the paper. My eye was caught by an advertisement which, by a felicitous coincidence, applied exactly to my case: 'Are you suffering from gastric pains? Do you feel depressed? Take some AZOTYME.'

I immediately wrote down the name of the panacea. But when I asked the chemist at York the next morning how I should take the medicine, he stared at me. The advertisement that had caught my eye was addressed to the dog population of Great Britain—to greyhounds, bulldogs and fox-terriers, to the exclusion of all animals of my species.[1]

It was snowing hard when I reached Pickhill, near York, the country house of Colonel Basil Cranborne, where the Major was expecting me.

'My dear Daninos, your breakfast is waiting for you in the dining-room,' Marmaduke shouted to me from the top of the stairs. 'Basil's gone off to the vet. I'm almost ready—I'll be with you in a moment!'

---

[1] Advertisements in English newspapers are addressed to dogs, cats and horses (their respective communities being always referred to as 'populations') as much as, if not more so, to men. 'Can you go out on a day like this?' runs the rain-pelted streamer of a poster which in France would advertise a woman's raincoat. But here it is a cat, his tail raised like a question mark, which asks the question from behind a pane of glass. And it's another cat that answers him: 'Yes . . . because I use TIBS. So take some TIBS, my dear; you will feel completely refreshed.' *Tibs, a vitaminized product, makes cats frisky.*

Even for advertising beer, whisky or soap, the leading firms make their appeal to the (human) public through the medium of seals, penguins or kangaroos. Nothing like them to attract the eye of an Englishman! If a technicolor film star asserts that such and such a depilatory cold cream is marvellous, that's fine; but if it's a walrus that gives its solemn word, it's even better.

While waiting for the Major, I listened to the radio giving out the latest news. An unusually heavy snowstorm had blanketed the British Isles during the night. In many places villages were isolated and human lives endangered. This was followed by some political news. Then, after a moment of silence, one of those beautifully modulated, reticent and distinguished voices—the trademark of the B.B.C. announcer—came on to the air to make the following appeal:

'Do not forget that the snow keeps the little birds from finding their food. So put out little bits of bread, bacon and cake crumbs in your gardens. Put out bowls of water. Please think of the little birds!'

There was another moment of silence, during which I expected to hear an appeal on behalf of the homeless—the influence, no doubt, of listening to the Abbé Pierre. Instead, it was jazz music which now came on and stayed on.[1]

'Hello, old boy!' Major Thompson cried, as he greeted me. 'Well, had a good journey? . . . But where are the Pochets?'

When I told Marmaduke of our separation, his hearty laugh boomed through the quiet dining-room. The Major agreed that they had gone a little too far, but 'after all, they were very valuable dogs'. I advised him not to say that sort of thing to Madame Pochet next time he saw her.

'But, my dear fellow, we regard animals as superior beings no doubt just because you treat them as inferiors. They don't possess that wretched thing which makes us commit so many idiocies—speech. When you think what circumlocutions we

---

[1] It would seem that the British radio and television closely follow the wishes of at least one reader of the *T.V. Mirror*, who wrote in a letter to it: 'I suggest that the B.B.C. introduce a programme from 7 to 7.25 a.m. entitled, "Pussies' Half-Hour", during which we would hear nothing but animal voices, and above all bird songs. I am convinced that such a broadcast would greatly help to *quieten* our dogs and cats, who are so often sad or nervous when we are watching television.'

Paul Morand, that fine connoisseur of the English animal, relates that when he was on the staff of the French Embassy in London, every spring the Embassy would get a note from the Foreign Office requesting the French Government to take all possible measures to ensure that the little migratory birds returning from North Africa to the North would not be shot down on their flight by the inhabitants of Southern France.

employ to avoid stating the bald truth, how could we not feel an unbounded admiration for beings who never say anything at all? Even with the best will in the world the most tongue-tied Englishman will always remain inferior to a dog, because sooner or later in his life he will be forced to say: "How do you do?"[1]

'Is that,' I asked, 'a reason for showing more tenderness to an animal than to a child? One of your masters can break his cane on the back of a public school boy, and no one will say a word of protest. But if I break the leg of a dog that has bitten me, I may end up in prison.'

'Well, you'd at least have the whole neighbourhood, not to say the whole country, against you. There's only a National Society for the protection of the young, whereas there's a Royal Society for the protection of animals. The difference is significant.'

'And you find this normal? A psychoanalyst——"

'You and your logic! Next thing you'll be giving me that damned nonsense suggesting that "The tenderness we refuse our children we lavish on our Pekinese." There's some truth in all that, but a lot of nonsense too. I won't deny that we think it less ridiculous to stroke a cat than to pamper a small boy. We bring up our boys severely because one day they must become men. We pet a dog because it will always remain a child. Besides, we don't really cajole him; we simply play with him. We love playing. We adore dogs because you can play with them right up to their dying day. Take Colonel Cranborne, for example. His wife has got the flu, and he's gone to see the vet."

'You mean that he is having her treated like a horse?'

'Certainly not! But he's in a far greater rush to get someone to look at his old Newfoundland, which is stretched out in the warmest and most comfortable room in the house, than he is to fetch a doctor to look at the boring old flu of his wife, who is asleep in an icy bedroom. But that doesn't keep us from being a lot more sentimental than you think. Look at what's going on

---

[1] This is certainly the opinion of a Justice of the High Court who exclaimed in the course of a recent trial: 'If there are no dogs in heaven, I don't want to go there!'

'JAMES, WOULD YOU PUT ON ANOTHER CAT. I FEEL A SLIGHT DRAUGHT.'

right now—from the Orkneys to Guernsey all Britain is worked
up over the happiness of her Princess—at the idea she can't
marry the choice of her heart. Or take that forbidding Jennifer,
whose heart, you think, is made of stone, because of the way she
maintains a Spartan discipline dear to Mrs Cripplestone. Do you
know what her first thought is on a winter morn when it's bitter
cold and she's shivering under her thin coat. "Let's hope the
Queen's well covered!" Only usually we hide this sentimental-
ity beneath a cold exterior. It's what you label with that stupid
word "hypocrisy", which you use as a sort of master key for
unlocking us. At least it's something we reserve for our equals.
For animals the barriers are lifted and we can give free rein to our
feelings.'

'Your admiration for animals does not keep you from hunting
foxes——'

'Rubbish! We never shoot them! It's a contest between
them and the hounds. How can you understand the intoxication
that seizes hold of an Englishman on an autumn day when he
hurls his horse across the countryside, jumping stream and bush,
fence and hedge in full pursuit of a fox? He draws all England
into his lungs. And everyone is happy—horses, hounds,
men——'

'And the fox, too, I suppose?'

'Yes, even the fox. He enjoys the sport. He plays. . . . It's
only the last minute or so that can be a bit nasty for him. Too
bad! But where's the cruelty in all this? The really cruel thing
would be to deprive those stout dogs of a meal after they've run
a hundred miles.'

The Major always knows the answer.

That Major Thompson's countrymen should be more concerned with the fate of animals than of men was borne in on me
in striking fashion on the very day I landed in England. The
catastrophe at Orléansville had just aroused a worldwide wave of
sympathy, and I was thus not surprised to see on the front page
of *The Times* a little announcement, the first line of which was
written in capitals:

EARTHQUAKE IN ALGERIA. SEND CON-
TRIBUTIONS IMMEDIATELY

But it was to the Royal Society for the Prevention of Cruelty
to Animals that donations were to be sent, for as a result of the
earthquake thousands of mules, horses, cats and dogs had been
made homeless. Of human victims there was not a word.

Some days later I attended a debate in the House of Commons
with Major Thompson. Facing each other across the floor and
in front of the bewigged Speaker, the M.P.s from both sides of
the House were engaged in a bitter battle of words in that
traditional parliamentary style which allows one man to call
another a fool only after he has preceded it with the word
'Honourable'.

'What,' I asked the Major, 'is the subject of this violent debate? The atomic bomb, nationalized industry?'

'Myxomatosis, my dear fellow.'

What was at issue was not the danger of contamination, since
myxomatosis is not transmissible to man (besides which, no
Englishman worthy of the name eats rabbit), but the peril that
this scourge represented for English cats, for which rabbit is a
favourite dish. The honourable members were doubly aroused
because of a dockers' strike, which had prevented the unloading
of merchandise in British ports. No one was worried by the
prospect of the British starving. The uproar was over the fact
that the strike had stopped delivery of frozen meat from Aus-
stralia, the only suitable food for cats since the outbreak of the
myxomatosis epidemic in Europe.

It so happened that the next question on the agenda was
poliomyelitis. Instantly passions subsided. Several M.P.s went
out to have a cup of tea, and the problem was dealt with in an
atmosphere of general indifference.[1]

'If animals had a Pope,' Major Thompson said to me, 'their
Vatican would be in London. And if by some dire submarine

---

[1] I am not inventing this, a pity though it is. I refer the conscientious reader
to the *Daily Telegraph* of December 27th, 1954, which emphasized the contrast
between the heated nature of this debate and the dullness of the one that followed.

cataclysm that noble vessel, Great Britain, were to be ship-wrecked, believe me there would surely be somebody in Westminster to cry from the top of the Tower: "Dogs first!"' [1]

[1] I could go on endlessly citing examples to prove that the English harbour a secret sympathy for the cat-o'-nine-tails when it comes to men, while lavishing bucketfuls of tenderness on animals, even of the most revolting sort. One night I was in a Piccadilly cinema watching a documentary film on underwater fishing in the Mediterranean. The film showed an Italian frogman being seized by the tentacles of a giant octopus, from which he managed to free himself only after the most dramatic struggle. He finally succeeded in running his harpoon through the body of the monster, whose black blood darkened the sea. The lady sitting next to me, who had not shown the slightest feeling for the diver, could not, on seeing the octopus mortally wounded, keep herself from clutching her neighbour's arm and murmuring: 'Poor little thing!'

Even when they are their hapless victims, the English can't bring themselves to complain of the behaviour of animals. Never for a moment did it occur to them to kill the gorilla in the London zoo which tore off the arms and caused the hideous death of an imprudent child. Of a less serious nature was the bite which the dog of a celebrated actor took out of his master's lip, but it was still serious enough to keep him off the sets. Attempts were made to stifle the truth, and the first communiqué announced that the film star was suffering from lung trouble. The actor, however, changed his mind. 'I wanted to conceal what actually happened, for Charlie [a four-year-old Kerry Blue] is heartbroken over what he did. . . . The truth is I asked him to kiss me, but he was a bit too passionate.' (It cost him two stitches and a week out of action.)

'GIVE ME ITALY, PLEASE!'

FACTORIES FOR GENTLEMEN

THE English, who tenderly employ the feminine for their battleships, leave their children in the neuter. In a land where it is often easier to determine the gender of a man-of-war than that of a man of the world and where the number of sexes is definitely greater than two, this neuter is at once prudent and significant.

This is not to say, of course, that the English, though they don't cherish them like their dogs or deck them out like their yachts, are lacking in affection for their children. Their peculiar way of displaying attachment is by detachment—by severing themselves from their children and having them brought up by specialists. This may seem odd, but in a realm where the animal is king, what greater homage could a Briton pay his children than to have them brought up like horses?

Not unlike those owners who, to compete in the Derby, must sign up their colts at birth, the English enter their progeny as soon as they come into the world in the registers of those venerable gentlemen stud-farms Eton, Harrow and Winchester. Here they learn far more about jumping hedges, taking a thrashing, running a steeplechase and curbing their instincts than about becoming, like the Latins, 'thinking steeds'. The secret of these public schools—which, as the name implies, are private institutions where one pays dearly for the privilege of being beaten, as opposed to the state schools, which are public institutions where one pays nothing to escape corporal punishment—is not so much the sharpening of the intellect as the forming of character.

I was with Major Thompson one fine spring morning when he

was trying to explain all this to his wife, Martine. We were visiting Eton as a possible choice for Nicholas's schooling. Through
the quiet streets of the old town ruddy-cheeked boys in black
tail-coats were sauntering along, their hands in their pockets.
On meeting a master in his black gown, they would take one
hand out of their pockets and salute him in the traditional manner
with a negligent forefinger, the master responding, according to
tradition, with an even more nonchalant finger. The boys that
were not in tail-coats wore striped blazers, grey flannel shorts and
caps, and were bound for the playing fields, armed with cricket
bats and oars. Through the tall lancet windows of a neo-Gothic
hall we could see three boys taking a 1929 Rolls to pieces (practical work instruction). Otherwise, at three o'clock on this
Monday afternoon, the classrooms were empty.

'So this is what you call education, *mon Marminet?*' remarked
Martine ironically.

The Major, who seemed elated to find himself once again in a
familiar haunt of his youth, gazed up at the sky for a moment
and then said:

'It would be interesting to know if God created spring after-
noons for the young to extract square roots in dusty classrooms
or to play cricket on these vast lawns. Martine, dear, when I
think that the Almighty can at one and the same instant behold
the young girls of Wycombe Abbey issuing from their "houses"
to play lacrosse and those of the Lycée Victory Duruy in Paris
closeting themselves indoors to calculate the surface area of the
cone, I think I can guess which way His heart inclines. . . . Your
young children, at the end of a school year, look like ailing
septuagenarians, whereas our septuagenarians have the faces of
schoolboys. In France, really, you don't go in enough for
sport!'

'In England you do too much . . . and because you do too
much, you produce *des imbéciles*!'

'Ridiculous!' spluttered the Major. 'Another of your absurd
prejudices against English education! Meredith noticed, and I'm
convinced he was right, that there are about as many fools in
England as in France. But an English fool is a fool pure and

'AND NOW WE OLD BOYS WILL SHOW YOU WHAT WE HAD TO TAKE
WHEN WE WERE AT SCHOOL!'

simple, whereas a French fool is a fool who reasons.[1] The English are sometimes ignorant; but their strength lies in not knowing it. That's a damned sight better than being highly intelligent and too well aware of one's weaknesses. It's reasoning that ruins people at the critical hours of their history. Hitler had two hundred armoured divisions at his command and the continent of Europe under his heel at a time when the gentlemen of the city were still doing the arms drill with their umbrellas in the streets of London. Any reasoning animal could have envisaged the inevitability of their defeat. But there wasn't an Englishman worthy of the name who entertained the notion for an instant.'

Martine grew thoughtful for a moment.

'All right,' she said, 'but in any case I won't have Nicholas caned—any more than I could bear to have you follow the matrimonial advice of the Reverend Father McCaskill by giving me a *fessée*[2] every now and then.'

Martine, it should be said, had been deeply stirred that same morning by several things she had read in the *Daily Express*. The first was an article expounding the theory of conjugal bliss of a Presbyterian minister. ('From time to time it is a good thing for young couples to inflict punishment on each other. Certain complexes won't stand up for long under a spanking.') The second was a dispatch appearing under the bold headline:

THE HEAD CANES 200 BOYS

In it the newspaper told how the head of a school, having failed to discover the author of an obscene drawing that had appeared in the school porch, had decided to cane every boy: two hundred strokes on two hundred outstretched hands. The newspapers had immediately sent their reporters to get the story —not from the boys but from the headmaster. The headmaster, worn out by an arduous day, was resting, so his wife undertook to answer their questions.

[1] The Major himself didn't hesitate to say one day about the members of the Cavalry Club: 'Some officers are so stupid that even their brother officers notice it.'
[2] 'Spanking.'

'Of course Peter's arm aches, but you can say, at any rate, that he would have done the same thing with his own children.'

When the punished were interviewed in their turn they displayed not the slightest bitterness but rather a certain admiration for the athletic prowess of their headmaster. 'He really is tough,' said a fourteen-year-old student. 'He kept up the same pace for twenty-five minutes non-stop. Mine was the two-hundredth hand and I can assure you that the last blow was as hard as the first.'

'Altogether an exceptional case,' said the Major, somewhat put out. 'The proof of it is that the newspapers reported it.'

'Well,' said Martine stubbornly, 'I do not want my son beaten, even *exceptionnellement* by someone I do not know."

'Then he'll never be a real gentleman.'

'I do not see the connection.'

'You'll never understand the first thing about us, my dear. It's from Eton, Harrow and Winchester that our leaders come, the élite. And what is the first duty of a leader? Self-control. And what is the first thing one must learn in order to control oneself? Being controlled by somebody else.'[1]

---

[1] London still boasts a Society for the Propagation of Corporal Punishment, and *The Whip through the Ages* is still prominently displayed in the windows of orthopaedic shops round Charing Cross. It must be said, however, that corporal punishment is much less frequent in schools than formerly. It is reserved for serious misdemeanours. The headmaster administers the punishment by appointment, and his authorization is necessary for a thrashing of any kind. The pupils themselves are the first to defend the system. A teacher at a London school recently asked his pupils which they preferred—being kept in after hours or being caned— and an overwhelming majority was in favour of corporal punishment, on the grounds that it is sooner over and gives an opportunity for showing courage. When a woman journalist dared to stigmatize these 'Spartan methods' she was smothered beneath an avalanche of protests. A thirteen-year-old schoolboy wrote her: 'When I read your article to my schoolmates, they burst into howls of laughter. Would you like each of us to have his own little Teddy Bear? Everything you say is utter nonsense. We are all very happy.'

According to the statistics collected by Geoffrey Gorer, the author of some remarkable studies of British behaviour, most English parents are in favour of corporal punishment, some of them even displaying in their application refinements that Freud would have delighted in. A father of three children, who approved of wholesale punishment for both sexes, notably recommended 'spanking in the presence of other children to humble the self-esteem of the wrongdoer'. A fifty-seven-year-old father in Wolverhampton suggested that naughty boys should be

In learning self-control, the young Englishman can rely as much on his seniors—prefects responsible for maintaining discipline—as on his masters. Nothing could be better for a future lord or for a governor-to-be, destined one day to rule the peoples of Bechuanaland and Uganda, than to begin his career as the slave of a sixteen-year-old boy who can call on him, as a fag, to make his toast (without a toasting-fork, naturally), to carry messages at the double to another prefect, to polish the floor and to climb a rope. Public school education seems to have been designed to allow every boy one day to become Viceroy of India. Their India has gone, but the old methods remain. In the period of his life in which he is reduced to servitude, the future gentleman may well express an unfavourable opinion of the public schools. But in the first place he is not asked for his opinion, and in the second he is afraid of looking ridiculous if he gives it. And, above all, he waits with confidence for his hour of revenge—when, having himself been bullied, he can bully in his turn. Never would it occur to an Etonian or to a Harrovian to write home a tearful letter telling his family of the caning he has just had. He would lose face for life with his family, his fellows and himself. A real gentleman never complains. He knows how to take it. This is a law the English obey all their lives.[1] From canings to freezing dormitories and rationing, the Englishman accepts everything without grumbling, and the moment some regulation—a matter of national necessity—forbids him to eat more than 8 ounces of meat a week, no one would dream of eating 8·1 ounces. It wouldn't be cricket.

---

dressed up in little girls' clothes. Such was the variety of corporal punishments he ran into that Gorer undertook to draw up a synoptic chart showing the relative penchant of fathers and mothers for this or that speciality: (a) caning; (b) thrashing; (c) punching; (d) birching; (e) flogging.

[1] A French doctor, Dr Lugnier, of Marcilly-sur-Seine (Marne), recently wrote me of the following incident, which he witnessed in December of 1955: 'A young couple (French wife, English husband) suddenly lose an eight-month-old child (neurotoxicosis, dead in forty-eight hours). Gathered around the cot, French family sheds hot tears. The husband's mother arrives—typically English mien. The French sobbing is redoubled. "You are crying," she says to the mother of the young woman. "Don't you want to cry?" the other replies. "We cry," says the impassive Englishwoman, "but only at night." '

Does this mean that these people don't enjoy good food, hot water, or comfortable beds? No. But they enjoy even more perhaps showing the world that they can do without them.[1]

Whenever an indignant mother or an over-zealous reformer launches a campaign in favour of the abolition of corporal punishment, *The Times* receives a flood of letters from aged gentlemen who proudly recall the times when they were beaten. A septuagenarian will write: 'I shall remember to my dying day the time I was beaten because, as a first-year man at Harrow, I had buttoned only two, instead of three, of my coat buttons. It was a lesson I am still proud to have received.' At a ceremony at Haileybury College, Earl Attlee himself recalled with some pride how he had been one of eighty-two boys who had received a caning in 1900 as a result of a rowdy demonstration.

An Englishman's first dominion is the one he must maintain over himself. Be master of oneself to be master of the world—such is the spirit in which the boys are brought up at public schools, whose first aim is the manufacture of gentlemen. But it would be a mistake to think that only the public schools, reserved as they are for the sons of the well-to-do and a few scholarship-holders, go in for this kind of manufacture. The humblest English schools share the same ambition and their students model their manners on those of the famous schools. In this land where the workman copies the lower middle-class man, who copies the upper middle-class man, who imitates the aristocracy, which takes its cue from the sovereign, who shakes hands with the workman—everyone aspires to *gentlemanize* himself.

But just what is a gentleman?

For the French a gentleman is someone who kisses a lady's hand and gives up his seat to a woman on the Underground. But this summary notion has little to do with the idea of a gentleman in England, where ladies' hands are never kissed and where a man who wants to give up his seat risks being put in his place by a woman who feels she does not need such marks of condescension.

[1] The more famous a school, the more uncomfortable it is.

The definition of the perfect gentleman was enunciated back in 1440 in the statutes of All Souls College at Oxford, the highest university authority in the realm: *Bene nati, bene vestiti, et mediocriter docti.* (Well born, well dressed and moderately learned.)

This definition remains essentially valid in a country where intelligence is considered an insidious disease that only an indefatigable discretion can palliate. It is, however, inexact as regards clothing. For a country labourer a gentleman is somebody who on Sunday can allow himself to don a pair of patched-up trousers with a tie around his waist for a belt. For a workman a gentleman is somebody who sounds his aitches and wears a bowler hat on weekdays.[1] For a gentleman, a gentleman—someone who dies without even pronouncing the word—is a man who climbs Everest, never mentions it to a soul and listens politely to Pochet's account of how in 1937, and in spite of his sciatica, he conquered the Puy de Dôme.[2] In a drawing-room a gentleman must above all avoid talking of what he knows most about. If he did so, he would be taken for one of those experts or professionals so much abhorred by the English—those sturdy champions of the amateur. An Englishman who wishes to be a physician must work hard to become a *Doctor*; but he must work even harder to re-become a *Mister*. It is the great privilege of surgeons to be once again called *Mister*, like everyone else.

These ways of speaking, dressing, behaving, of treating war like sport and sport like war are learned, or rather, contracted, like some healthy malady, by these gentlemen-to-be first at the public school and then at the university. For manners are not so much learned as transmitted—by contagion.

---

[1] Summary, though not inaccurate. If I could do it, or rather if he could reach it himself, I would have Daninos crash that 'sound barrier', so audible to the aristocratic ear and which allows us, by sole virtue of an *h* or an *o*, to determine the social origins of an individual. It would be a good idea, in this connection, to undertake a geological survey of English society, beginning with the Foreign Office crust, the bowler stratum, and the neolithic substratum of mustachioed Majors-in-retirement. Suffice it so say for the moment, and until I can find the time to devote myself to these new excavations, that with us the stratification of classes is such that it applies even to dogs. A publicity folder for an hotel in the seaside resort of Torquay says: 'Dogs are charged for at the rate of 1s. 6d. to 3s., according to the size and social standing of the dog.' (W. M. T.)

[2] A 4500-feet hump in Central France. (W. M. T.)

Torn at the tenderest age from the bosom of the family,[1] the English child is placed in one of those medieval nurseries called public schools and reared on the great feeding-bottle of tradition. There is only one way of wearing a straw hat at Harrow, of saluting the masters at Eton, of walking (in groups, for solitude is frowned on) for the young girls at Wycombe Abbey, and of carrying primers and exercise books at Charterhouse. There is only one way, everywhere, of sleeping and working, winter and summer, rain or shine, with the windows wide open. What does it matter if it is a good or bad way? It is the one which was adopted three hundred or six hundred years ago, and that is all that matters. What does it matter if studies are less important than sports? The floor of the room where the boys of Harrow take their first steps as gentlemen is made from the oak of the ships of Trafalgar. The history of Napoleon can perfectly well come after cricket; it permeates their skin by osmosis.[2]

On benches where Peel and Gladstone have carved their names, the young boy grows up convinced that all that is best in the world is British—ships as well as woollens, secret service as well as zoos, butlers as well as aeroplanes. Take the climate. The children of Albion are taught that England is an ideal country with a temperate climate; its inhabitants are the only ones who know it.[3]

[1] It would appear that English children take their revenge on their parents when they grow up. Heartlessly banished to freezing dormitories and canings, the young later get even with their elders by packing them off to grim boarding-houses, like Mrs Cripplestone's, where, solitary and abandoned, hundreds of thousands of ageing Englishmen and women end their days on a diet of cabbage soup.

[2] The history of England is accorded a far greater place than that of other peoples in the mind, as in the education, of English public school boys. I realized this one day when I attended a history class at Harrow. The form master kindly let me ask some questions of his students (fourteen and fifteen years old). I asked them which French King it was that was guillotined. 'Louis the eleventh,' said the first. 'Louis the twelfth,' said the second. The sixth got the answer right, and Mr Harris called the game off. I then asked them who had burned Joan of Arc, and they all replied in chorus: 'The French.' We took leave of each other on good terms. All these boys looked healthy, happy and friendly. Out of twenty boys, only six had been caned.

[3] Only with regard to music are the English prone to be more modest. Speaking of the Albert Hall, renowned for its acoustics, Sir Thomas Beecham once said: 'It's the only place in the world where English composers stand a chance of hearing their works twice.'

In the shadow of high brick walls and on the green carpets of century-old lawns, the young Englishman is marked with an imprint that nothing will efface. When, for seven long years, you have been accustomed to living with eight hundred boys, to making the same gestures, observing the same rites, putting on the same clothes, obeying the same rules and practising the same sports in the same team spirit, you bear an indelible stamp. No matter what career he chooses, the Englishman throughout his life carries on him the hallmark of his school, and he seizes on the slightest opportunity to re-immerse himself in its beneficent waters. When you have noted the joy with which the Bishop of Willesden abandons his cross and his mitre and dons his old school cap and shorts, in order to go out on the Thames to umpire the Oxford–Cambridge boat-race, you can better understand that the English are born gentlemen and die children. The septuagenarian who proudly writes in to *The Times* about his first caning is not an old man; he's an Old Boy.

Beneath the prelate, beneath the statesman lurks always the schoolboy. Both apply to the affairs of the world the solid principles of cricket, club and school. When Churchill said to Stalin that to be a member of the 'Great Powers Club' one had to have an entrance qualification of four million soldiers, it was Harrow speaking to Yalta. It was a septuagenarian super-prefect, wrapped in his gown of tradition and privilege, laying down a new Marquess of Queensberry rule. When the former Home Secretary, Major Lloyd George, spoke of a possible settlement with the Russians and the Chinese, he began by inviting these people to play cricket: it would simplify everything. And when Mrs Cripplestone wanted to explain Hitler to me, she said: 'The trouble with that man Hitler is that he never went to a really good school.'

BIBLE, BRIDE AND BRITON

'To open an Englishman,' Major Thompson once said to me, 'there are two master keys: whisky and the Bible.'

As I don't always walk around with a Bible on me (or with a bottle of whisky, for that matter) many Englishmen remain a closed book to me. But one day, while reading the Sunday paper, I realized just how right the Major was. British Sunday papers are very important for the proper understanding of the English. Here you can read everything, and in the greatest detail, that the English dare not say out loud (the French say it, but wouldn't dare write it). And in this way, with some twenty million fellow readers, you can easily scale the supposedly inviolable walls surrounding Mr Smith's private life.

In this particular case Mr Smith was called Mr Jones. He was a cuckold husband. In France this type of person inspires the writers of comedies, but in England he inspires sympathy. What had happened was that Mr Jones had undertaken to read his wife the fifty-first Psalm—the one in which David repents of having committed adultery with Bathsheba. This had been too much for his wife who, afflicted by a bad conscience and a good memory, had thereupon confessed to having deceived him thirty years before. And as though this blow weren't enough, she had gone on to inform him that his son Eric was not his own. Mr Jones, in truth, might well have suspected as much, for the fact was that to use the legal formula he had never 'consummated'. His leisure evening hours were almost exclusively devoted to reading the Bible in the company of his wife. Fervent Baptists both of them, they attended public readings of the Scriptures every evening in the parish of Bermondsey.

It was on to this tranquil scene that there suddenly erupted

William Henry West, an equally faithful member of the Band of Hope. These healthy evening distractions must have failed to satisfy him, for one day, returning unexpectedly home (normal husbands return home at normal hours, but deceived husbands always come home at impossible hours), Mr Jones found Mr West with his wife. The least that can be said is that they were not reading the Bible, though they were at least literally applying the basic commandment: Love one another.

Whether it was through greatness of soul or for some other motive, the fact remains that Mr Jones did not provoke a row, but simply remarked to Mr West that in his estimation he had no business behaving this way with his wife. Some time later, as she was accompanying her husband to the train at St Pancras (English trains themselves never stray too far from the Scriptures), which was to take him to Manchester, Mrs Jones told him that she was pregnant. As Mr Jones had made no approach to her for the past five years, this appeared a bit odd to him, but the train's departure interrupted the course of his reflections. When he returned home, his wife, who had gathered together a formidable mass of documentation, persuaded him that it is possible to have children without what the English so poetically describe as 'sexual intercourse'.

Mr Jones consequently raised no objection to recognizing Eric as his son. Most of the Bermondsey parishioners remember a man who was very happy the day the child was born. He must have been a little less so when rumours began to reach him that Eric was not his son. Still, as a worthy citizen of the land of wait and see, he had to wait twenty-five years before obtaining a frank explanation by way of the Scriptures. He then decided to sue for divorce and to lay the blame for it on his wife and her co-respondent (a word used by the British to designate a lover, and which is, after all, not particularly shocking in a country where the vocabulary of love owes more to the Chamber of Commerce than to the Kama-Sutra, and where a liaison is called an 'affair').

The judge, however, refused to accept Mr Jones's claims and even sentenced him to pay the costs, including the travelling expenses incurred by the lover. As for Mrs Jones, she stayed at home and there it was that that same evening Mr Jones found her—this time alone and once again ready to read the Bible.[1]

[1] This story clearly attests the Bible's importance in the daily life of the British, who find everything in it: consolation, hope, explanation, recreation. It quite often happens that in the midst of naval manœuvres (between two rival comands) an Admiral and a Vice-Admiral will exchange semaphore messages quoting passages from the Gospel according to St Matthew. It would be quite a job just to count up the number of English societies whose only function is the distribution of the Bible. There is even one, with headquarters in London, which calls itself the Society for Distributing the Holy Scriptures to the Jews. It is well-nigh impossible to spend a day in England without coming into direct or indirect contact with the Bible—even if only in the personal column of *The Times* in which appear quotations from the Bible (of which the Authorized Version of 1611 is regarded as the perfection of the English language) or messages to Heaven. Assuming the Good Lord and the Saints to be subscribers to *The Times*, many pious English people, whose prayers have been answered, choose this way of bringing their thanks to the attention of Heaven, with such two-line messages as: 'To Saint George with the expression of my gratitude and thanks. J. N. W.'

MARTINE AND THE ENGLISH

 I THINK it's high time I took up the pen again to set matters straight. This Jones story, singular as it sounds, has occurred more than once in England, I'll grant you, but it shouldn't lead anyone to believe that we British never 'consummate'. There's nothing I distrust more than this French mania for generalization.

Come what may, the English will always look upon the French as frivolous, sex-obsessed people. The French, for their part, will always regard the English as refrigerators, persuaded as they have been, ever since Stendhal, that we feel an urge once a fortnight and grow bored in the interval.

Boredom—always that confounded word!

Anyone who has watched a real honest-to-goodness Englishman snoozing in his club or dozing through a cricket match will have to admit that he savours his boredom as a Frenchman his little game of *belote*.[1] The only thing that really bores an Englishman is having somebody come along and bore him while he is happily boring himself. For there's nothing he enjoys more than relaxing in a state of complete vacuity. At such moments his mind is a vacant site, and the last thing he wants for it is a tenant.

Now how the devil can I ever get this into Daninos's head? Or how, for that matter, can I ever make Martine realize that when she sees my old friend, Arthur Palethorpe, sitting alone on a shooting-stick in the middle of his Kilmarnock woods, he is anything but bored and is in fact engaged in his favourite pastime—bird-watching? The game I enjoyed most in the world—cricket—bores Martine to distraction. '*Je trouve ça d'un long!*' she says.[2] Well, I'll admit that it can sometimes be a bit long

---

[1] Card game much played in French cafés.
[2] 'I find it terribly tedious!'

drawn out and that a match may go on for five days—there was even, I recall, one memorable engagement in South Africa that lasted a whole week without really ending, the British team having to re-embark before its conclusion. But what of it? When I see a good bowler bowl a good length spin, it positively tickles my spine.

I should thus be sorry if this Jones business were to give Daninos a false impression. The truth is that our women were greatly changed by the war. A mighty tidal wave arose to sweep away the old conventions. The corset of Victorian prejudices split open. By allowing her to drive generals up to the firing-line (or not far from it), the war created a new species—the man-woman. Today women are all over us. You find them everywhere—conducting the buses, in Parliament, in the police force. . . . They even pursue us into our clubs, where they are now often admitted one day a week.[1] Some of them even behave with more abandon than American women. The twentieth century will go down in history as that which witnessed two great explosions, each of which, in its own way, brought new suffering to men—the explosion of the atomic bomb and that of the Englishwoman.

Pochet got an inkling of this one day when he saw a lovely London 'cover-girl' called Gwendolyn kiss on the lips a Frenchman that she hadn't known an hour before.

'*Mais alors . . . mon cher Major*,' Pochet said to me, 'what about your stories of Lady Plunkett enveloping the legs of her grand piano in muslin and advising her daughter, the night before her marriage, that when the time came she should close her eyes and think of England. . . .'

'It's obvious, my dear fellow,' I said to him, 'that you'll never understand the first thing about us. It's because there have been and still are Lady Plunketts among us that you run into Gwen-

---

[1] By the side door and for limited periods only. On the days they are admitted to the dining-room a kind of no-man's-land of empty tables separates them from the tables occupied solely by men—thereby limiting the effects of this promiscuity. When I expressed my surprise that the members of the Reform Club should be waited upon by women in red dresses and white caps, the Major said: 'What does it matter? For us here, women are preceded by a minus sign.' (P. D.)

dolyns. They make up the two faces of Britain—one of them severe and puritanical, the other libertine and brazen. We still have people who consider it bad form to speak of what lies between the neck and the knees. We still have colleges where flirting is considered ridiculous.[1] The aim, if not the effect, of British education is to put children to sleep without allowing them to dream. And yet every day in some part of England a Lady Chatterley throws a county into an uproar. And when the devil gets into an Englishwoman, nothing stops her, not even the sancrosanct barrier of classes. Here, look at this. . . .'

I could do no better than hand him a copy of the paper, which told of how the heiress to one of the oldest families in England had eloped with a groom eighteen years her senior who could neither read nor write.

Now it would be just as dangerous for my friend, Daninos, to generalize in the opposite sense.[2] The Englishwoman is emancipating herself, to be sure. Formerly matters pertaining to sex were banned from conversation, condemned by modesty. Today people are much freer in their love making, but without talking about it any more than before. At heart, our country hasn't changed. Here, as in Shakespeare's time, you can still write the most beautiful love sonnets. But it remains a man's country. And in this man's country, where everything is done for men, nothing delights a woman more than to be taken for a man. She dreams less of being adored than of being independent. Her latest conquest is the trouser—to such an extent, indeed, that

[1] In certain Oxford colleges undergraduates are divided into three categories: (1) those interested in neither men nor women; (2) those interested in men; (3) those interested in women. It was not so long ago that the Fellows lost their privileges as Senior Members on getting married.

[2] Was the Major perhaps afraid that I would bring up some embarrassing comparisons? It is curious to note that in an interview the stable-groom declared: 'What drew us together most was our love of horses.' Now *twelve months earlier* the Major had written in his Notebooks, apropos of his first wife, Ursula: 'It wasn't so much love that united us as a passion for horses that brought us together.' The Major and his translator (myself) at that time received a number of letters from irate Englishmen. 'You exaggerate,' they said. 'Our women like horses, no doubt, but not to the extent of resembling them or marrying out of love for these noble beasts!' This groom, who had not, for obvious reasons, read *Major Thompson Lives in France*, thus refuted them in his turn. So true it is in life that with the best will in the world one can invent nothing! (P. D.)

IT IS SOMETIMES DIFFICULT IN ENGLAND TO KNOW IF IT'S A MAN
OR A WOMAN ONE IS UP AGAINST

it is sometimes difficult for a foreigner in certain public services to decide if he is dealing with a man, a woman, or both.

Yes, my dear Pochet. With us in England love does not flow through the air as it does in your gentle land of perdition. Walk around Paris in the springtime and you can feel currents of love all about you. A pretty woman going by is in permanent contact with a thousand eyes. Even the most spoiled husband looks at her with the eyes of a lover. But here there is none of that kind of silent complicity of persons and things which makes the atmosphere of Latin countries so propitious for sentimental adventures. When a Paris policeman makes out a summons for a young lady motorist, he is not exactly the same as when dealing with a man. He tempers the law with an indulgent complicity. When a salesman shows off a pair of gloves to a Parisienne, there is love in the way he sings their praises, in the way he asks her to try them on. The English, on the other hand, think of one thing at a time—the summons, the gloves or love. Never the three together. All your French country inns look as though they were harbouring clandestine lovers. The *patronne* is on your side. '*On vous comprend . . . on sait ce que c'est, allez . . . la vie est si courte . . .*'[1] The *patronne* may well have three children herself and know that Monsieur is the father of a family, but youth is fleeting . . . particularly at the age of fifty. In England we have none of those inns with names like The Seven Capital Sins or The Forbidden Fruit, where all is allowed. The omnipresence of the Bible and the vigilant eye of the manageress, ever ready to pounce on illicit couples, will quickly suffice to give you that guilt complex which Pochet complained about. And yet there is love in England. The love of animals. The love of flowers. The love of gardening. The love of sport. The love of the Navy. The love of the Royal Family. Everywhere there is love—but it isn't just to be found in love, in *l'amour*. In the British order of things love is an element that takes its place among others. It has to be fitted in somewhere.[2]

---

[1] 'We understand . . . we know how it is, eh? . . . Life is so short. . . .'

[2] To be exact, in seventh place, as far as the relations between men and women are concerned—if we are to trust the statistics drawn up by Geoffrey Gorer, who

This is not to say, once again, that Englishmen are unsentimental, but because their love goes first to the nation, to sport and to animals, the Englishwoman has to take what is left. Besides, most of our authors have held women in pretty low esteem—even feminine authors. 'I have never had much use for women,' wrote Mary Wortley Montagu, 'and my only consolation in being one is that I can't marry another.'[1]

One radiant April morning Martine and I were walking through Hyde Park. Blue and white nurses were taking out pink and white children. Riders were galloping under the leaves. A few cocker spaniels were gambolling on the grass. A sorrel ridden by a young Amazon shied, throwing her rider. Galloping on for fifty yards, she ran straight into a fence and rolled over. A hundred people promptly rushed towards the horse, barely five towards the lady.

'*C'est bien ça!*'[2] Martine exclaimed. 'You can walk all nude around London and no one will pay attention to you—unless you are accompanied by a dog.'

Never will Martine get used to the apparent indifference to women of Englishmen and to not having men's eyes linger on her, above all when she goes out, as was the case that morning, in a Balenchy suit. In France women dress as much for themselves as for others. The same coquettish spirit is seldom found among Englishwomen, who like to be at their ease in 'sensible' shoes and who display in their way of dressing a greater taste for nature and bright colours than a concern about men. Against the greyness of the weather they react with torrents of green and red. To counter the rain they put sunlight in their mackintoshes. Little does it matter how they will appear to men, since nine times out of ten they won't appear to them at all.

---

asked a cross-section of English womanhood the qualities they looked for and appreciated in a husband: understanding (33 per cent); attentiveness (28 per cent); sense of humour (24 per cent). Love (14 per cent) was sandwiched between generosity (17 per cent) and tolerance (13 per cent). (P. D.)

[1] This celebrated *bon mot*, which dates from 1723, was picked up seventy-three years later by Madame de Staël. I have no idea from whom Mary Wortley Montagu got it.

[2] 'That's just like you!'

Some time ago one of our journalists launched a campaign against the hideousness of the uniforms worn in certain of our boarding-schools for girls, where they are condemned to wearing black stockings, rough serge pinafore dresses and floppy purple felt hats with green ribbons—when it isn't red hoods lined with mauve. She received innumerable protesting letters, among them this typical one from an indignant mother: 'Uniforms are made to be worn, not look at.'

One day Mrs Cripplestone undertook to explain all this to Martine, but far from convincing her, she left her thoughtful.

'Martine, dear,' I said, 'you seem sad. I don't like those clouds in your eyes.'

'It's your country that is sad, Marminet. Your country has no eyes. I put on an *amour d'un tailleur*[1] this morning, but no one looked at me.'

Mrs Cripplestone gave a little cluck.

'Tut tut, my dear. When I was young and pretty—for such was once the case—I used to take the train from Wimbledon to London and I had the impression I bothered everybody. The men would entrench themselves behind ramparts of newspapers, the women would cast disapproving glances at me, and the guard never spoke to me. But now that I am inoffensive everyone is nice to me. The men no longer hide their faces, the women look at me kindly, and the guard speaks to me. I feel much more comfortable.'

And Mrs Cripplestone, a kitchen garden on her head, now moves gaily through life. She no longer even thinks of 'defending herself'. Why defend oneself in a land where no one attacks?

Mrs Cripplestone's case left Martine more baffled than ever. Later I explained to her that this was by no means an isolated case. Often in the very éclat of her beauty there is something provocative which bothers an English girl more than it delights her, and rather than stress it, she does her best to tone it down.

When I ask Martine, 'How do you find Englishmen?' and she answers, 'Darling, I do not find them', I'm neither surprised nor

[1] 'a little gem of a suit'.

particularly shocked. After all, she did find *me*, and I don't see
why she needs try to find any others.

The trouble, however, is that here in England Martine—so
at least she claims—can no longer find even me.

'When you are in your own country, Marminet, you are no
longer the same man. *On dirait que tu as peur d'avoir l'air
d'aimer.*'[1]

Good Lord! It's not so far from the truth. But how on earth
could it be otherwise? Martine has difficulty enough getting used
to my dashing out for the evening paper to see if our bowlers
have taken any more wickets in the Australian Test Match, or to
my putting on a blazer and shorts to join some Old Boys on the
Thames. But she gets more than her revenge by asking Lady
Hoburn, while tweaking my moustache with her little finger or
pinching my crimson cheek: 'Don't you think, Lady Hoburn,
that he looks like a big cat?' How can I help being shocked?
And how can I be expected to hear myself called *Marminet* in
front of Lord Redboon without feeling horribly belittled? These
are trying experiences for an ex-Indian Army officer. I know I
put up with them in France, and I even get a certain kick out of
them. But here! when I think how simple it would be just to
call me 'Mahrm'diouk', like everyone else, instead of '*Diouki-
Diouki*'!

Martine realizes this clearly enough and it exasperates her.

'If it bothers you, just say so. If you feel uncomfortable with
me in the presence of the Duke of Tcheechestaire,[2] I can go
home, you know? If you think it is always pleasant for me to
listen to what they say in Paris about your moustache or your
impossible Christian name!'

When the argument reaches this point, I usually prefer to
avoid battle and, beating a prudent retreat, to *filer à la française*.[3]

---

[1] If I were to translate this literally as 'One would say you are afraid of giving the
impression of loving', Daninos would probably hold it up as a proof that even
English syntax suffers from cumbersome inhibitions. I prefer to leave it untrans-
lated.

[2] Normally pronounced 'Chich'st'r'.

[3] 'To take French leave', the normal equivalent of which in French is, as one
might expect, *filer à l'anglaise*.

There are moments when one must know how to contain oneself, even at the risk of blowing up. After all, Martine isn't altogether wrong in 'looking for' men in this island. Englishwomen themselves have trouble enough finding them, not only because education directs them to the wicket rather than to women,[1] but also because the men are less numerous. By some ironical design, which even the most assiduous reading of the Bible can hardly explain, God has seen to it that in this country where they do not especially attract the attention of men, more and more women should be born every day. Frenchwomen are all like Martine. When they get to London, they complain that no one looks at them. They simply don't realize that in crossing the Channel they lose fifty per cent of their value.

I must ask to be forgiven; if I speak of women in the language of stockbrokers, it's not altogether without reason. The Englishwoman is like Royal Dutch Shell: she obeys the law of supply and demand. In a country where there's a surplus of three million females, the market quotations are bound to sink. Though we don't have an official market here, as they do in Timbuctu, you can get a pretty good idea of the current prices from the reports of recent divorce cases, the market quotations for Englishwomen being proportionate to their household value. For the purposes of this valuation nothing is neglected by our courts—neither housekeeping, cooking, nor laundering. In France a husband who has been abandoned by his wife can get a divorce, but he won't seek to estimate his loss in financial terms. With us it boils down to a question of *damages*. 'Mr Smith claimed a thousand pounds. Taking into due consideration the value of the wife and the damages incurred by the husband, the judge split the difference and awarded him five hundred pounds.' That was how the *News of the World* reported a divorce suit. But it's only

[1] Hardly a day goes by without some Englishwoman lodging a complaint with the courts because her husband has been neglecting her for cricket or football. Not long ago a woman sued for divorce on the grounds of 'mental cruelty' because her husband had been devoting almost every Saturday and Sunday to cricket and football. 'No sooner is he back from the office than he bolts his supper and rushes off to play.' The judge, however, rejected her complaints, 'the law not allowing a man to be declared guilty of cruelty for liking cricket too much'.

H

natural, isn't it, that in the land of fair play the lover should foot the bill?[1]

Well, it may be natural for us—but it's not for Martine. When I explained to her one day that my good friend, Colonel Nigel Lesspot (now retired), had sued his daughter's husband because she married while still a minor and without his consent and that he had won his case by proving to the judges that Priscilla's departure had forced him to engage a housekeeper, Martine exclaimed: '*Pays de sauvages!*'[2] Yet Colonel Lesspot was altogether within his rights. When an Englishwoman abandons her husband, it's not just a wife that he's losing in the eyes of the law; it's above all a housekeeper. Thus it is that on passports or identity cards, where, opposite the entry: *profession*, Martine writes *sans* (none), an Englishwoman writes *housewife*.

'*Décidément*,' Martine says to me, 'it's not the same *planète*.'

Yes, a strange planet this, where, incredible as it may sound to Martine or to Madame Pochet, a wife can sue for divorce on the grounds that her husband has raped her.[3] A strange planet where I one day heard a headmaster thus define the ideal wife to his senior boys: 'A faithful companion, a nurse, a mother and a loyal friend. . . .'[4]

[1] Quite apart from the 'utilitarian' value of his wife, a deceived husband can always claim from the co-respondent—his rival—damages for 'loss of *connubium*'. There are times, it must be said, when the magistrates are loath to make a precise value estimate of a wife. 'To have to estimate the value of a wife in pounds, shillings and pence is often delicate and rather nauseous,' a judge declared during a divorce trial where a Squadron Leader claimed five thousand pounds from the co-respondent for depriving him of his wife's company.

[2] 'Land of savages!'

[3] I myself saw a woman obtain a divorce at a London court by explaining that her husband, entering her bedroom by an unlocked door at a time when she was unwilling, had assaulted her (an exceptional case foreseen in the Matrimonial Clauses Act). When the repentant husband spoke of unsatisfied sexual desires, the judge advised him to find some substitute: 'Why not collect butterflies?' (P. D.)

[4] It was the day of Edward VIII's abdication. The headmaster, who was as grave-faced as he was embarrassed—for the height of embarrassment for an Englishman, when something happens, is to be unable to find a precedent for it—had assembled the boys to hear the King's farewell on the wireless. On the desk of the great hall was placed a large Bible. Having defined the perfect wife, the headmaster added: 'There exists another kind of wife, that one should ever be on one's guard against. . . . Listen to what St Paul says about marriage.' After

'WHAT I REALLY LOOK FOR IN A WOMAN IS A PAL!'

A pal! In France palliness kills love. In England a woman is above all the pal of the man. When a French girl says to her boy friend: 'Let's remain friends!' it's the end of everything. Here it's the beginning of the rest.

---

reading the misogynous apostle's apologia for celibacy, the headmaster switched on the broadcast.

This schoolmaster's definition of the ideal wife may seem peculiar, but it agrees fairly closely with the statistics. Among the chief qualities Englishmen look for in their wives, beauty, elegance and sex appeal are only mentioned by a very small number (8 per cent) and most of them bachelors, at that. The qualities of 'good housewife' (29 per cent) and 'good mother' (18 per cent) rate far higher. It is not difficult, therefore—at any rate for an Englishman—to understand the comment made by a judge who, having to decide a divorce case in which a wife complained of neglect by her husband, declared with a straight face: 'The marriage was a happy one, apart from a sexual matter which was always a difficulty.'

Strange planet, where in her heart the wife often has a secret garden—the garden of *Brief Encounter*, to which her husband never has access unless one evening, in the quiet of the home, the reading of the Bible opens its gates!

Strange and inexplicable planet! Perhaps there is even a mystery about this island that I myself cannot explain. Famous biologists have noted it. An islander is different from a continental—whether flora or fauna. If Britannia built her future on the waves, it wasn't only, as some humorists have claimed, because more children are conceived on a Saturday afternoon on the Thames than anywhere else at the same time. Nor was it for love of the Royal Navy. It was because an Englishman, never finding himself more than sixty miles from the sea, is subject to the influence of the tides even in the Underground. The day that some barbarian conqueror finds a way of lowering the level of the Channel by a hundred and fifty feet in order to attach this island to the continent, we shall doubtless become, for Martine and the Pochets, normal people with normal looks. Heaven grant that this day may never dawn and that the continent may for ever keep its distance from this unexplainable island-planet!

Dear old England, whose charm and dampness penetrate simultaneously. I came back to rediscover you all-repentant and prepared to crave forgiveness from the shades of my ancestors for the affront I offered them in making France my home. I would have liked to stay here longer and spend more time treading the century-old lawns. Above all, I should have liked Martine to appreciate . . . But she, like Pochet, is not yet ripe. We must wait and see. . . .

While waiting, I am once again going to abandon dear old England. It's a funny thing how much a subject, and even more a servant, of Her Most Gracious Majesty can absent himself from England, until the day finally comes when he absents himself for good. For the moment my fate is linked to that of Daninos and Pochet—and Pochet's got itching feet. Each spring some paper reporting the imminent plunge of a bathyscape or a new assault on a Himalayan peak produces the same effect on him as does on millions of sun-starved Britons the official announcement of the first cuckoo reported to *The Times* by some retired army colonel in a Shropshire wood. Speleologists and frogmen arouse in this hearth-loving Frenchman a slumbering explorer, and he suddenly wishes to participate in the vast movements of discovery that are agitating the globe. While Alpine climbers and navigators polish up their instruments for assaulting the Great Unknown, Pochet purchases new suitcases and departs for the conquest of lands long, long submerged—by floods of people. He whose father dared extend an adventurous spearhead as far as Pamplona and San Remo now speaks of Stromboli as though it were Mont Dore! Oh, how the French animal has changed over the centuries! England, of course, no longer suffices to satisfy this wanderlust; it is at once too near and too remote. Pochet's desire is to go farther and farther afield, and above all farther than Taupin. Fortunately his thirst for travel is quenched easily enough in the bottomless well of his business operations. For Pochet's business activities are the most accommodating in the world; they always take him just where he wants to go. He combines business with pleasure. Thus, having heard that our friend Daninos was planning a trip to America, he suddenly discovered a thousand 'business' reasons for visiting the United States.

And so there's nothing for it, I'm caught up in the wheels of this transoceanic operation. I have given him every possible warning on the basis of the experience of others, but Daninos is still bent on trying to fit the United States into the Anglo-Saxon world. To keep my part of the bargain I must go with him and be on hand to help him. After all, if I feel nothing in common with the great American democracy, I have nothing against it either.

And then there's another thing—Daninos and I have never really agreed when it was a question of our two countries. Something tells me we may come closer to doing so by joining forces to criticize a third.

THE MAJOR AT SEA

IF ever there was a time in his life when the Major was visibly at sea, it must have been during our transatlantic crossing on the s.s. *United States*. No sooner were all on board and our things safely stowed away in the cabins than he set out with Pochet on 'an initial reconnaissance of the bar'. He was back in half an hour with the announcement that he wanted to go upstairs for a last breath of fresh British air, so I offered to accompany him.

'It's a remarkable thing, Daninos,' he growled, as we emerged on the promenade deck, 'but I never thought I'd live to see the day when I'd feel like an alien in a British port. It's right here in Southampton that I've discovered the United States. Just look at this great liner that is taking us to New York. It's simply crawling with specimens from all forty-eight States. This motley array of tourists, many of whom you will notice even have their national eagle stamped on their bags, are like lovers who having paid their dutiful respects to old Aunt Britannia and flirted a bit with the Latin Sisters return to their first love—delighted with their Grand Tour, but happier still to be back among their own kind and on their way to regain the only really serious country in the world: the most powerful, the most prosperous, the most beautiful, the United States of America.'

It seemed strange to me that the Major should feel such a foreigner among fellow Anglo-Saxons, and I pointed out to him that there were after all strong affinities of blood and language binding together Britain and America. He cut me short:

'My dear fellow, how on earth do you expect me to feel any affinities for people who call me "Marm" the first time we meet and ask me how many thousands of copies my latest book has sold? As for the language——'

'Now, you cannot deny that you speak the same language?'

'Yes, Daninos. I do deny it! I deny it completely! Indeed, it's probably the one thing we have in common that most divides us. I was given a shocking example of it a moment ago. What is it, my dear fellow—does my English sound snobbish to the American ear? Just imagine—at the bar a few minutes ago the steward, a Yankee thoroughbred, if I may be permitted such an outlandish expression, instantly understood Pochet's order, but made me repeat mine!'

I could see by the glint in his eye and the bristle of his moustache that the Major was really launched, so I made no effort to halt him.

'Yes,' he went on as we paced the deck, 'it's really incredible! This country, which hadn't even moved into its present abode when we had already been settled for a thousand years on our island, has borrowed our language. That's bad enough, but after giving the most awful twists to our speech they now have the nerve to pretend they don't understand us! It's utterly absurd! In fact, I'm told that to hear proper English spoken in the States you have to go to the theatre!'

'I don't know,' I said, 'but I remember reading somewhere a remark by the American dramatic critic, George Jean Nathan: "After thirty years in the theatre I am still wondering if our actors talk and behave like Englishmen, or if Englishmen talk and behave like actors."'

'So he did, did he? Just wait, I'll deal with this Mr Nathan,' muttered the Major. 'I never heard such nonsense!' he exploded after a moment's silence. 'How can you say Americans talk at all? Just listening to the passengers on this ship I get the impression that it's not so much words as figures that fall from their lips. Ever since I got on board I've heard them do nothing but exchange souvenirs of their trips to Europe. Foreign tourists often exchange souvenirs that no one can figure out, but these souvenirs have nothing but figures in them! "In Florence I bought a clip for ten dollars!" . . . "Look at this one—it's exactly the same, only red. I paid eight dollars and twenty-five cents for it

in Rome. There was another just like it in blue and black for
nine dollars——" ... "And how was your one-month trip?"
... "Oh, simply marvellous! We stayed five and a half days in
Paris, three days in Florence, four days in Rome and two in
Venice. We usually did a museum in the morning and two
monuments in the afternoon. But sometimes Spencer would
want to change the schedule, and we'd do a couple of churches
in the morning and only one palace in the afternoon. Would you
believe it? We covered ten thousand miles! It was a nice trip![1]
In Florence we lived on the half-pension plan—they charged
5700 liras, but you can get along perfectly well on 5000. .... And
what about you?'"

This strange sensation of gobbling figures, which so struck
the Major the moment he set foot on the s.s. *United States*, was
accentuated with the first meal we took on board, for the con-
sommé was swimming with little numbers from 0 to 9. It was
further sharpened the following day when the Major and I made
the acquaintance of Mr Cyrus B. Lippcott.

Mr Lippcott is the kind of American of which there are many
—what am I saying? I mean 255,407. He looks a bit like Harry
Truman. He has the same glistening incisors, the same pursed
lips, the same frank glance from behind thin gold-rimmed glasses,
and if this dealer in grain did not, like the ex-President, get his
start in the world selling braces, he did none the less climb from
the bottom to the top rung of the Associated Pork Packers and
go on to become head of an important section of the Middle West
Corn Exchange.[2] He is clean, he is neat, his shirt is gleaming
white, his shoes are like two sunbeams, his suits are sober—only
his ties have something African about them. But why am I in-
troducing him, instead of letting him introduce himself, as he
did that first day when he moved his deckchair up alongside the
Major's and put out a welcoming hand:

---

[1] This word 'nice' never fails to crop up in American conversation and is one
of the dozen keywords in 'Basic American'. (W. M. T.)

[2] I might add to this description of Daninos's that the American *Who's Who*
will no doubt describe him in the terms usually reserved for prominent industrialists: *controls 1000 miles gas pipeline, 10 carbon black plants, also 3 gasoline plants,
etc.* (W. M. T.)

'Glad to meet you, Major! My name is Lippcott—Cyrus B. Lippcott.'

Reluctant as the Major obviously was to open up to a stranger on an American ship, there was nothing he could do to prevent the other from opening up to him. In short order the Major and I learned that Cyrus B. Lippcott would be fifty-one years old on 6th May, that he was born in Kansas City, Missouri, that he made 25,000 dollars a year, owned a six-room house in Schenectady, New York, had a 60,000-dollar life insurance policy, and that having first married a wife seven years his senior, he had remarried a second who was six years his junior. . . .

'And what about you?' he suddenly shot at the Major.

The Major was speechless for a moment, and I could tell by the startled look in his eye that he was wondering how on earth the English language—but was it English?—could be used to say so many things in such an incredibly short space of time. In less than four minutes Mr Lippcott had told us more about himself than a Frenchman does in four months or an Englishman in several generations. In reality, what interested Mr Lippcott more than anything was to know just how many tigers the Major had shot in his life: 8, 12, or 370?

'H'mm!' grumbled the Major, clearing his throat. 'Well now, I don't really know. . . . I've bagged a goodish number—that I can say for sure—but really, I'm not much interested in the number. . . . It was the fun of the thing, you know, the sport of it that mattered, that's all——'

'Sure, Major, but what would you figure on the average—two a year?'

'H'mm, h'mm,' mumbled the Major, visibly annoyed.

Seeing that he could get no precise information out of him, Mr Lippcott opened his pocket-book and pulled out a photograph of a young girl.

'Let me show you a picture of my younger daughter, Major. Her name's Patricia—isn't she a honey?'

'Oh, I say! Jolly fine!' mumbled the Major, awkwardly fingering the photograph, which showed a young schoolgirl wearing a sweater with the numeral 6 on it.

H 2

'Well,' Mr Lippcott went on, 'you'd never believe it, Major. She's only sixteen years old and she's already five feet five inches tall!'

'Five feet six inches, Cy!' corrected Mrs Lippcott, who had just joined us.

'Oh yes, darling! Five feet six inches! A real nice kid! She's got half a dozen boy friends her own age and she loves her college—2400 girls and boys in it, and think, it's only 166 miles from where we live, so we can see her twice a month. A real nice place!'

It was apparent from the Major's flustered expression that this first exposure to Mr Lippcott and his family was sufficient for the time being, and he got to his feet muttering something about 'taking a stroll' and 'getting his sea-legs'.

'Good Lord, Daninos,' he said when we were safely out of earshot, 'I need a good lungful of numerically unpolluted fresh air before I go down to my cabin.'

Unfortunately for the Major, there was no escape. The numbers pursued him relentlessly; when we stepped into the hall of the promenade deck we came face to face with a handsome blackboard on which the main events of the day were listed in bold white letters. The day's film was announced:

LADY CYNTHIA'S PASSION (112 MINUTES)
(EASTMANCOLOR)

'Well, if that doesn't take the cake!' muttered the Major. 'I can well understand an American needs to know that Lady Cynthia's passion is going to last one hundred and twelve minutes before going in to see a film on board ship. His time is limited, and he might have a train to catch. But my own indifference—on the Atlantic, or anywhere else—as to whether Lady Cynthia's passion lasts a quarter of an hour or an hour and fifty-two minutes can only mean one thing, Daninos, and that's that I'm just not made to be an American!'

THE NUMBERS-MEN

THE impression of living among numbers-men was one which I, no less than the Major, was to experience not only on the boat but often afterwards on the terra firma of the United States.

Cyrus B. Lippcott, with whom we had struck up a friendship despite the basic antagonisms between him and Marmaduke, had arranged to meet us in New York, whither his business affairs often bring him. We were to meet on the appointed day at the Park Lane Hotel. The first thing that struck us in its monumental bar was a sign which warned us:

The Presence
of more than 388 persons
in this establishment
is dangerous and unlawful[1]

The Major made a rapid panoramic survey of the room, no doubt to estimate the number of persons present—it was not 388—and then ordered a whisky. He was brought a bottle of Grant's Scotch, the name of which was printed on a white label marked: 4,207,680 minutes. Why 4,207,680 minutes? Because the chief merit of this whisky is to be eight years old, and for an American 4,207,680 minutes make eight years as easily as four times eight make thirty-two.

Mr Lippcott, however, expressed a preference for champagne. 'Bring me a Chandon-Moët 52,' he said, after pulling out of his wallet a curious little card covered with figures where Bor-

[1] I say 388, and not 350 or 400, and I invite the sceptics to visit the Park Lane and verify the figure themselves. It may mean a bit of a trip, but it's worth it.

deaux, Burgundies, ports and champagnes were rated from o (no good) to 7 (the best) for the years 1931 to 1955.

'You see,' he said to me, '52 rates a six, so it's O.K.'

This made me think—the Major too, and especially Sonia, who being used to saying when she gives me a telephone number, 'It's Trocadero 82 something,' or when she speaks of the population of the United States: 'They're a good 120–150 million, no?' is here completely out of her element. She is just not made of the same stuff as Mr Cyrus B. Lippcott, who never speaks of a Picasso, but of a 30,000-dollar Picasso; who doesn't talk of a building, but of a 2-million dollar building, a 75,000-volume library, or a 38-room château. Even of a man he will often say: he's a 150- or a 500-dollar-a-week man. All this the Major accepts with a smile, though it goes against his grain. What he cannot stand is hearing Lippcott say of his poodle: 'He's a 700-dollar dog, you know.'

Never, Marmaduke insists, would a well-bred Englishman dream of mentioning the price in the presence of his dog.

Europeans are sometimes shocked when an American, who has been introduced to them barely a minute before, asks them how much they earn a year or how much they paid for their suit. The Major regards this as shockingly ill-bred. But he's mistaken. It's simply the result of a very different mentality and up-bringing. Not to declare your salary is to hide something from your neighbour and to display a lack of that spirit of mutual trust and co-operation which goes into the making of a 'hundred per cent American'. It's something you pick up at school along with the notion of numbers.

At that tender age when the French child learns that his ancestors, the Gauls, lived in huts built on piles and wore long handlebar moustaches, the American child learns that there were 102 Pilgrims on board the *Mayflower* when she sailed from Plymouth on 6th September, 1620, and that these 102 pioneers, after completing a voyage of 3200 miles in 66 days, were to grow into a nation of 166 million, with an annual budget of 66·3 thousand million dollars.

The American child may be late in learning to read, but he is early in learning to count. He has the billion in his bloodstream long before the alphabet.[1] At an age of forty and some years I still have only the vaguest notion of what their billion is. I must go to the dictionary to find out whether it is 2 million or 100 million. Every American child knows it as a thousand million, just as we French used to know that a *sou* (five centimes) was a *sou*.

Personally, figures have always wearied me. When the *New York Times*, for example, informs me that the revenue of the city of New York, for the first quarter of the fiscal year beginning 1st July, was $469,097,383, as compared to the $462,941,874 of the preceding year, I find myself swimming in a vast porridge of figures. If I were told it was $888,983,566 or $602,500,343, it would be all the same to me. I feel no urge to subtract one from the other to get the difference; rather I feel like subtracting myself from the subtraction to see if there isn't something else in the newspaper to read about. But it's no use; an American paper is the last thing to read if you want to escape figures. There are more figures in a single copy of the *New York Times* than in 700 copies of any French daily.

As a souvenir I have kept a copy of the paper I bought on the evening of our meeting with Lippcott at the Park Lane, when I came back to the hotel with my head still reeling with figures. Everywhere I looked I met numbers:

2 MILES OF PIERS SET FOR BROOKLYN IN 7-YEAR PROJECT
$85,000,000 JOB

FORD MOTOR COMPANY: $2,000,000,000 INDUSTRIAL
EMPIRE

PRESIDENT BETTER: 46-MINUTE TALK WITH
5 COUNSELLORS

[1] One of the largest and oldest banks in the United States, the Bank of America of San Francisco (nine thousand million dollars in deposits), distributes money boxes to high schools enabling students to open bank accounts as early as they want, the contents of the money boxes being collected each month by the bank. Most American children, rich or poor, earn their pocket money outside school hours either by delivering newspapers or by working as gardeners' assistants, grocery boys, caddies, restaurant waiters, etc.

CYRUS B. LIPPCOTT AFTER READING THE *New York Times*

Nothing escaped the all-powerful figure—neither the Pro-
testant Churches, which had distributed one thousand million
dollars through 3000 welfare agencies to succour 11 million
needy; nor the 5,200,383 inhabitants of the State of New Jersey,
who had taken orderly refuge in 63,483 air raid shelters in a civil
defence exercise announced at 6 p.m. by 809 sirens and supervised
by 250,000 wardens; nor the Ford Empire, now worth 2 thousand
million dollars after starting out 53 years ago on an initial cash
investment of £28,000; nor the 57,475 fans who saw the Lions of
Detroit trounce the Bears of Chicago when the 6 foot 9 inch,
21-year-old Jim Maloney plunged over the goal line on a 12-
yard pass in the game's fourth period for a winning score of
26 to 19; nor even the stomach of the late Wilson Woodward,
Jr, accidentally shot by his wife, the body of the 35-year-old
multi-millionaire sportsman being found to contain only 0·065
per cent of alcohol, whereas the intoxication level is legally fixed
at 0·15 per cent.

In the land of Cyrus B. Lippcott there is not a word, not a
gesture, not an act that cannot be reduced to figures. Everything
is measurable: the work of a writer ('Damon Runyon made half
a million dollars with 75,000 words'), the efficiency of the Catho-
lic Church, which, with a coefficient of 82·5 per cent, almost
equals that of Standard Oil, the maximum length of a kiss on the
movie screen (40 inches of film), or the number of calories needed
to read *Gone with the Wind*.

The United States believe in numbers as the Arabs in the
Koran. Thanks to numbers the Americans recently discovered
that the consumption of water in the United States between 9
and 9.30 p.m., which had remained constant for 35 years, had
noticeably increased in the last two. Why? Because of television. And why because of television? Because 60 million
Americans, being forced by the new Divinity to remain seated
from 7 to 9 in the evening, simultaneously use their bathrooms
from 9 to 9.30 p.m.

O *homo americanus*, you who are a number lost in a sea of
numbers, you live and die a number—from the $2000-a-week
executive to the $86-a-week guy. The composer, George Gersh-

win, once organized a dinner in Hollywood where the guests were announced by their weekly earnings. At a banquet given in honour of Pandit Nehru in New York to which the cream of American industry was invited, a businessman said to him: 'Do you realize, Mr Prime Minister, how much is represented at this table? I just added it up. You are eating dinner with at least twenty thousand million dollars.'

From the heights of the pyramids, forty centuries looked down on Napoleon's armies. From the lowliness of their chairs, twenty thousand million looked up at Nehru.

Even what I was doing at that very moment was, I discovered, numberable and numbered. For the *Christian Science Monitor* informed me that the average American absorbs twelve and a half inches of international news and a good yard and a half of sport news a day.

With the human eye eating up the page, it seems, at the rate of two-tenths of an inch a second, I was busy calculating—having become a real American—that our friend Lippcott must devour some 30 yards and 33 inches of comics every Sunday, when Major Thompson burst unexpectedly into my room.

'What did I tell you, Daninos, about these people having no manners! Look at this!'

He handed me a copy of the evening paper, whose flaming headlines announced:

MEG SAW G. C. 3 TIMES
157 MINUTES YESTERDAY

Actually, the Major was not particularly interested in the fact that Princess Margaret had seen Group Captain Townsend three times the day before and that they had talked for a total of 157 minutes. But that these Yankees should push familiarity to the point of calling the Queen's sister 'Meg' made him positively blow up.

WHAT IS AN AMERICAN?

I MUST make a confession: when I tell myself, on arriving in the United States, that there are 166 million Americans, that they could fit France 17 times over in their country, and that I must write something about them, I feel like going right back to bed in Paris. I am seized by dizziness. My eyes blur. I feel faint.

This time Major Thompson came to the rescue.

'Calm yourself, old boy! You're raising a storm in a teacup—the biggest teacup on the globe, I'll grant you, but what of it? You'll see, the United States is the most transparent nation in the world. The first couple of days here I too felt quite bowled over by the immensity of it all. The frightening thing, of course, was the figures—166,000,000 inhabitants! But you must never let yourself be overawed by figures. You may remember that when I had to size up 43 million Frenchmen I resorted to division. Here it's even simpler: a subtraction will do. Now there's nothing like a citizen of the Middle West to show you how to do this subtraction properly, and since you're lucky enough to find in our friend, Cyrus B. Lippcott, a native of Kansas City, Missouri, go and ask him to enlighten you.'

The Major, as usual, was right. For Cyrus B. Lippcott the centre of gravity of the U.S.A. and of the solar system is Kansas City. And the heart of America and its flesh and soul is the Middle West. The rest is peanuts.

It took Cyrus a bare half-hour to clear up the situation. To deal with 166 million Americans he employed the method of the Indian head-shrinkers. He took out a bag of Michigan flat beans and spilled them out in front of me on a large table, giving them the approximate shape of the United States. Then, having crunched up Alaska and a few Aleutians—to be excluded from any significant representation of the U.S.A.—he began his demonstration:

Take a total population of	166,000,000 inhabitants
(a) New York not being the United States, we must begin by excluding from the total the population of this city and its huge suburbs, making	15,000,000 inhabitants
(b) Given the strangeness and abnormal behaviour of the people of Texas, who give their Lone Star flag precedence over the Stars and Stripes, they too have no place in any generalization about the United States; so let's be on the safe side and count out these	8,000,000 inhabitants
(c) The Bostonians—capable of telling you exactly the quickest way of getting from Piccadilly to Buckingham Palace, but needless to say incapable of telling you where Kansas City is, and only too happy to misspell 'Oklahama', as well as most of the inhabitants of New England, who are more English than American—obviously cannot provide any serious basis for a picture of America, which allows us to subtract another	9,000,000 inhabitants
(d) The Negroes, the Germans, the Italians, the Chinese, the Japanese and the really Jewish Jews cannot either be considered pure-blood Americans, so we must not include in the addition these	22,000,000 inhabitants
(e) Nor can we include in the total those Americans who, though American citizens, were born abroad, that is	10,000,000 inhabitants

(*f*) Certain borderland states, like Alabama, Arizona, Oregon, Montana, New Mexico and North Dakota, though an integral part of the United States, can only give foreigners an inexact picture of the country. So better omit their   9,000,000 inhabitants

(*g*) For different though equally valid reasons, the far too cosmopolitan populations of such cities as Washington, D.C., Hollywood, or Chicago, as well as those like San Francisco and New Orleans, which are full of Spanish, French and Asiatic elements, can only obscure a proper view of the real United States. So we knock out another   7,000,000 inhabitants

(*h*) For pure form's sake, we'll make a passing reference to the Indians, carefully shut up in their reservations, and who for having been the first comers are now the lowest of Americans. We can take out this residue of   350,000 inhabitants

Which means we must subtract from the total	80,000,000 inhabitants
There are now left	86,000,000 inhabitants
among whom we must eliminate all minors, aged and impotent citizens, or some	44,000,000 inhabitants
Which is as much as to say that there remain by and large (or rather by and small)	42,000,000 inhabitants

Barely the population of France, minus Montmartre and Montparnasse! You see, the U.S.A. isn't really such a terrible problem after all.

Still, even if we limit the number of real, *genuine* Americans
to 42 million, how are we to define the *homo americanus*?

Even the Major was a little reticent when I put the question to
him. I had doubtless attributed to him affinities with his distant
transatlantic cousins that he just didn't have. He was certainly
right about the language: it divides them rather than unites
them. And what the United States have done to the language of
Shakespeare, they have done to their people—they have americanized them. The great mystery and miracle of this country are
how, more than any other, it marks the individual with an indelible stamp, whether he comes from Frankfurt, Budapest or
Amsterdam. England makes you reserved, Switzerland numbs
you, France makes you lighter, Germany heavier, Italy makes
you gesticulate, Sweden makes you healthy, Spain ennobles you,
Ireland superannuates you—but the United States makes you
American.[1] As though after a mighty shuffling of chromosomes,
they put out their product on an assembly line.

The little emigrant from Budapest arrives at the start of the
conveyor belt stoop-shouldered, scrawny-muscled, black-haired,
anxious-eyed. He then undergoes the treatment of milk and the
wide open spaces, free enterprise and orange juice, the dollar and
the carrot, facts and figures. Vitaminized, deluxized, sanforized,
orlonized, simonized, chlorophyllized, fluidized, classified,
labelled and asepticized, the new arrival undergoes a metamor-
phosis. The American way of life transforms him. And at the
end of the assembly line, a generation and a half later, out comes
the finished product—a blond, long-boned, lean-necked, narrow-
hipped, milky-faced, short-haired Barbara or Johnny, all ready
to chant on 'I' day: 'I'm a hundred per cent American!'[2]

A mystery, all right—though a mystery that is doubtless explainable in terms of environment, the effect of the climate, cross-
breeding, high schools, food, and still more by that strange

[1] With the exception, of course, of British subjects. As Alistair Cooke has
noted, one speaks of Irish-Americans, German-Americans, Polish-Americans,
Swedish-Americans, Italo-Americans, Greco-Americans, but never of Anglo-
Americans. (W. M. T.)

[2] 'I' day for 'I am an American' day.

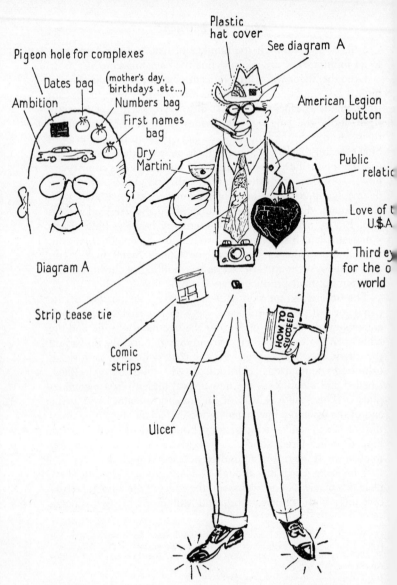

X-RAY PHOTOGRAPH OF MR J. H. S. W. . . ., AMERICAN CITIZEN

phenomenon of mimicry and the emigrant son's haunting fear of
not becoming American, talking American, thinking American.

Still it's a mystery.

How can I doubt for a moment that our friend Cyrus B.
Lippcott is not himself the product of this mystery? But defining him is none the easier.

O Cyrus, you who bear in your veins the blood of the Mac-
Cullaghs and the Finkelsteins, a pint of Alpestrini and of Mon-
tezuma, a bowlful of Ehrenkreuz and a drop of Dupleix, how can
I possibly define you?

How can you define a citizen who had a grandmother that was
Irish, another that was German, an American father, and a Dutch
mother, unless it is by comparing the cross-section of his brain
to that of our Chamber of Deputies—Ireland occupying roughly
the place of the Social Republicans, England that of the Communists, Germany that of the M.R.P., and the Jews that of the
Poujadistes?

I sometimes explain the stern side of your character by recall-
ing that one of your ancestors was a certain Patience Peacock[1]
who came over—and how proud you are of it!—on the *Mayflower* (no doubt about it. Yet if the *Mayflower* had really carried
all those whom present-day Americans swear by, she would have
had to be as big as the *Queen Elizabeth*).

You doubtless get from that Finkelstein, who began his career
selling braces on the street corners and ended it on the top floor
of a skyscraper as the Underwear King, your astonishing aptitude
for making good in grains after going bust in pork. I can see that
it is to Signora Bianchetta Alpestrini, your grandfather's wife,
who was the daughter of a Catania greengrocer, that you owe
your predilection for *pasticciata* and the Sicilian restaurants of
Greenwich Village. But how can I fail to admire the way in
which so many heterogeneous origins have managed to bring
forth products as specifically American as you and your blonde
child, the aerodynamic Patricia, whose voice, bearing and look
have something in common with millions of American high-

[1] The Puritans were wont to give their daughters virtues for Christian names:
Patience, Chastity, Fidelity, Silence.

school girls? What do you yourself now have in common with
those first colonists who made your country?

Those frontier wood-choppers, those pioneers, those blizzard-
hardened trappers who scorned the English love of comfort,
have become cold-shunning citizens more comfort-mad than
any Thompson. Those austere Puritans, who once condemned
all unnecessary talk about cooking, now like nothing better than
belonging to a club of Gourmets-Connoisseurs and having their
film stars' favourite dishes shown them on T.V.[1] These would-
be settlers, many of whom travelled six thousand miles to find
new lands into which to sink new roots, now move ceaselessly
from one home to the next (thirty-two million Americans change
their addresses every year).

Those individualists who abandoned their families, their
homelands, their customs, to go and live alone and far from
everything, now have a passion for doing everything in groups:
'Join us for a drink'. . . . 'Join us for a party'. . . . 'Join us for a
vacation.' Solitude is a plague. The solitary individual is suspect. The American is judged a singular being if he doesn't
know how to live in the plural. Let him drink, go out, sing,
travel, amuse himself and even shave—but never alone! Pochet
discovered this one morning on the Chicago–Los Angeles train,
when Cyrus B. Lippcott hailed him and a fellow passenger with
a: 'Join us for a shave, Al!' Whereupon he dragged the bewil-
dered Pochet into a washroom where half a dozen Americans
seemed delighted to be brushing their teeth, taking showers and
shaving together.

Have the Americans perhaps become the opposite to what they
were?

Those democrats who made equality the cornerstone of their
constitution are today maniacs of discrimination. It is relatively
harder for a young girl to gain admission to the Baltimore
Débutante Ball than to be received at Buckingham Palace, and
Madame Pochet, who thought she would have no more trouble
obtaining invitations to the Assembly Ball in Philadelphia than

---

[1] 'What could be more appetizing,' as Mr Fred MacMurray himself declared on
the radio, 'than two fried eggs proudly casting their limpid gold eyes upon you?'

'NEVER WILL I GIVE MY DAUGHTER AWAY TO A MAN WHO HAS BEEN AMERICAN FOR ONLY THREE CENTURIES!'

she does for the Annual Ball at the Élysée in Paris, had to repack her *lamé* evening gown because she was related to no direct descendant of one of George Washington's officers. She swore by Lafayette that never again would she set foot in that city where a colonial dame, armed with a formidable social register, had treated us to an exercise in subtraction even more impressive than Cyrus B. Lippcott's, since she reduced the number of bona-fide Americans to 2733. For many people in the world the height of distinction is to know as many people as possible. But for certain Philadelphia and Boston ladies the be-all and the end-all of life is to know nobody, or at least to recognize nobody as being anybody.[1]

In American conversation the words *exclusive, most exclusive, restricted* recur so ceaselessly that Pochet sometimes wonders if the secret dream of Cyrus B. Lippcott isn't the creation of an ultra-private club, a club so private that all Americans would be excluded from it but himself. For those lovers of independence who fled the strict etiquette and the humiliations of the European palaces suffer today the frustrations of nobility in a principality and would gladly exchange their blast furnaces for a title as they desperately pursue the thing they most lack—an aristocracy.[2]

[1] The Philadelphia lady in question, having carefully scrutinized the list of those invited by the Kelly family to the reception organized in Philadelphia to honour Grace's future wedding, exclaimed delighted: 'I know none of these people!'

[2] Lacking authentic quarterings of nobility, Americans resort to such substitutes as: the numbering of the descendants of famous dynasties (Henry Ford II, J. D. Rockefeller III), the attribution of privileged seats in the choicest restaurants and night clubs (at El Morocco the 'Siberia' in the champagne room is 'high class'; at Sardi's the bench is *the* place to sit; usually the man seated nearest to the powder room is a nobody); the numbering of licence-plates (the lower they are the better—AC 1 is excellent); the classification of cars themselves (some even putting a Chrysler before a Cadillac, because its resale value being less it offers a better indication of the financial unconcern of the owner). Only rich and famous people can afford to run around in very old and small cars. In Hollywood there are barely ten actors who can use an M.G. without the risk of giving a false impression. Finally the Social Register takes the place of a *Gotha* or a *Burke's Peerage.* Certain States have their own aristocratic classification according to a fixed order of social or financial seniority; in Texas cotton precedes livestock, and both of them come before oil (*nouveau riche*). In most great cities the annual débutante balls are scenes of merciless battles fought out between the *nouveaux riches* and the stately dames of the Board of Governors controlling the admissions.

HIGH-TENSION HE-MEN

THE day after my night-time arrival in New York, I woke up next to a man in red who was looking at me sardonically. Such a thing always (for me it was the first time) produces a strange impression. It's something to come to New York expecting to wake up with a view of Rockefeller Centre and to find planted in front of you a man in red wearing a baseball cap and motorist's gloves.

I sat up with a jerk and opening my eyes wider I realized that the man was not exactly at the foot of my bed, but a few yards away; he was looking at me through the window from the top of a skyscraper that was going up on the other side of the street. I at once realized that I must abandon all hope of peace and quiet, and I decided to ask the management for another room.

On the north side the situation was much quieter. The first day at any rate. But at the crack of dawn on the second I was awakened by a mighty roar of trucks and cranes. They were starting to tear down the obsolete building opposite. It's the law of existence in New York: everything is going up or coming down—houses, jobs, gadgets, celebrities, topics of conversation. I still cannot decide which is the more ghastly of the two noises, but I think the roar of demolition is even worse than the racket of construction.

The former begins with the chatter of pneumatic drills digging into the ground and piercing the walls. Then immense cranes carry off whole floors. In the space of a few seconds I saw a living-room, a dining-room and two bathrooms borne away. It's so well done that you are surprised not to see anyone being carried off with them. You even wonder how all of it ever held together.

Preferring to hear and see people building rather than destroying, I went back to the wing I had previously occupied. Obtaining a room on the twenty-fourth floor I estimated I had a six-day start on the enemy (who was rising at the rate of one storey every two days). A friendly enemy, to be sure, for over Fifty-seventh Street I had established contact with the little man in red: he is called Benedict Camacho, is 37 years old, has 2 children, a 1955 Chevrolet, a 10,000-dollar life insurance policy, and makes 110 dollars a week.

Contrary to my stupid calculations, which had failed to take into account the all-American passion for breaking records, Benedict Camacho was yesterday once more on the same level as my table. At three in the afternoon he had overtaken me. To-morrow I shall only see his feet. I would gladly go up another floor, but mine is the highest inhabited one. Above me there is only the 'roof', reserved for parties, receptions and evening dancing. Which means that when the workers knock off at five in the afternoon (I don't know how those people get down from such heights, but they vanish in the twinkling of an eye), I have a bare half-hour of respite. At five-thirty the party begins—with jazz, and then with *cha-cha-cha*—which I find less than cha-cha-charming.

At any rate, according to my calculations (good or bad), in eight days it will all be over.

Major Thompson, however, proved less patient than I. He claims that it's dangerous to get to know people before they are properly settled in. Besides, he says he can't sleep comfortably unless he's sure of waking up in the same place the next morning. Marmaduke therefore left the hotel, declaring to the Desk as he went:

'I shall return, gentlemen, when you are finally built.'

And he moved on to the only city in the United States that is more or less bearable for a subject of Her Majesty's—Boston, that impregnable citadel of American Anglomania, which has managed to beat the British even at the game of numbering houses. It was thus that the Major discovered between No. 8 and No. 14 on Beacon Street a No. 10½ that left him open-mouthed. And as though this weren't enough, he then espied through its

long-paned windows solemn whiskered gentlemen snoozing in
deep black leather armchairs over copies of *The Times*—exactly
as though he were strolling past the Cavalry Club in Piccadilly.[1]

One can get used to anything in life—even to the hurly-
burly of New York. None of this would have mattered much if
it hadn't been for the electricity. Paris is regarded often mis-
takenly, as the *Ville Lumière*, but New York is really and truly
the *Ville Électricité*. It is, at any rate, the first I have ever really
made sparks in. In New York there is electricity everywhere—
in taxi doorhandles, in hotel doorknobs, between two sheets of
paper, in your hair, in the Major's moustache, in everything.[2]

When Sonia, who arrived several days after me, came up to
my room, she found me dressed in my pants and wearing gloves,
to say nothing of a little chain around my neck that kept me
down to earth. She immediately realized that something was
wrong. I explained to her that the air of New York was so dry
and saturated with electricity that the only thing to do was to be
properly earthed at all times.

'You're joking?' she said.

To prove to her that I wasn't I took off my gloves and em-
braced her. She immediately felt the shock and bade me keep still.

I then amused her—if I can so call it—making a few sparks,
just to convince her. I opened a closet here and closed a door
there. I have done many things in my life. Making electricity
is, after all, an occupation like any other, if only it weren't so
disagreeable. I was continuing my demonstration when the telephone rang. As I had forgotten to put my gloves back on I received the communication in the fingers.[3]

---

[1] The place in question was the Boston Athenaeum, a private library whose
1049 members find ample time to indulge in the favourite pastime of Bostonians—
genealogy—and to discuss the dates of their respective arrivals in the city. When
you ask a Bostonian how long he has been living in Boston, he replies quite simply:
since 1702, as though he and his ancestors were one.

[2] The air of New York is so dry that room humidifiers are in great demand.
Everything is so charged with electricity that the toll-bridges carry antennae
sticking up from the road to make contact with the chassis of each car, thus
sparing the toll-collector the pain of an electric shock as he picks up the fare.

[3] I can well imagine the reader's disbelief over this episode, and particularly
over this chain business. In his place I, too, would feel that the author had gone a

'You get on my nerves!' said Sonia. And she left to go shopping. New York, she assures me, has got some *formidable* things in orlon. She has even already seen some underskirts . . . 'and, you know, half the price of what they are in Paris'. It is really extraordinary how expensive Paris can suddenly become when a Frenchwoman wants to buy something abroad!

Apart from the electricity you find in your hotel room—which varies with the amount of steel used in the framework[1]—I always have the impression in New York of being plugged into a high-tension current. The sensation is aggravated if, as was my case, you have just come from Geneva. All of which makes me wonder if the best way to appreciate the United States is not to begin the trip in Switzerland.

Let me explain; when I arrive in Geneva, I feel an invisible hand slowing down my motor. I could almost swear that the stationmaster of Cornavin had given me a dose of quinine. In New York the dose becomes an injection of electricity. Something here speeds you up. No matter where you go, you go quickly (without running, which isn't done). There is a New York rhythm you fall in with immediately, whether you are going to buy pyjamas at Saks or to blow up the safe deposit vaults of the First National Bank.

bit far. Should I confess that I hesitated a long time before including it? 'That chain', I said to myself, 'will take a lot of swallowing.' In fact, many people smiled when I told them the story. Well, in reality the chain that I might have invented had already been forged in real life—so true is it that if there is real life in fiction, there is even more fiction in real life. To convince the sceptics let me refer them to a lecture given not long ago at the Western Reserve University Hospital by Professor George J. Thomas of Pittsburgh, the text of which was obligingly passed on to me (when I was already back in Europe) by Professor Jean-Marie Verne, a Paris hospital surgeon: static electricity in the United States brings death to more than a hundred persons a year, killed in operating-rooms by the explosion of anaesthetic gases. The simple rubbing of a nylon slip or the moving of an anaesthetic apparatus can cause a catastrophe. Many precautions are thus taken to limit—though they cannot entirely eliminate—the number of accidents. Each piece of furniture, from the operating-table to wheelchairs, must be connected to the floor by a small chain, and everything that is insulated from the ground must be linked to it by some metallic connection or by a wet cloth (including the person to be operated on, who can, if he rests on an insulating rubber mattress, become charged with static electricity).

[1] It also depends on your footwear, the leather moccasin leading the field.

Sauntering is something that has no meaning in New York. In Paris you saunter down the rue du Chat qui Pêche, wondering whether you are going to end up in the rue de la Huchette or come out on the Quai Saint Michel. But you don't saunter in a city where you are certain of finding Fifty-seventh Street between Fifty-sixth and Fifty-eighth. Who is tempted to write a poem on squared paper? You don't saunter along a railway track. You don't saunter in the land of the engine drivers.

Americans in general and New Yorkers in particular are human locomotives that go non-stop from seven in the morning till midnight. (The American wife is a super-locomotive that drags her husband after her at a lively pace, and the men must be sure to be firmly hitched on if they want to avoid accidents.)

One of the most revealing books on the American mentality is, in my opinion, a children's book called *Tootle the Engine*, by Gertrude Crompton. *Tootle the Engine* tells you more about the U.S.A. than Tocqueville, Fenimore Cooper, Faulkner and Hemingway combined.

Tootle is a young railway engine which, like every little engine in Engineville, goes to the Locomotive School and learns the A.B.C. of every well brought up little engine: stop at the red flag and keep to the rails. This is the way you become a great lady, I mean a great streamliner. Like many of her classmates, Tootle begins well. Her columns are straight and she sticks to the appointed line. And then one day, at the end of a term, just as spring breaks through all along the line, Tootle discovers the joy of running off the rails to pick daisies.

The Head Engine, I mean the Principal of the Engineville School, is very worried. After consigning Tootle to the depot, she decides to call a Town Meeting, throws a 'danger' signal, and swings into action. Tootle is allowed to come out again. Again she is seized by a longing to pick daisies, and she leaves the rails. But the moment she goes to pick a daisy, she meets a red flag. She goes over to the other side of the track, bends over again, and again a red flag looms up before her. Everywhere the hostile landscape bristles with red flags. All the flowers have become stop signals, for all the engine-citizens have co-operated

and banded together to bring Tootle back on the straight path.
Which she does on seeing before her the green signal of the open
track. She will be a great streamliner.

Tootle is America in a nutshell, with its conventions, its con-
formism, its 'danger' signals, the wailing of sirens, town meetings, co-operation, and above all, the train-spirit—the train one
must take, the train of life, the American way of life. The American lives on rails, and if he is ever tempted to go and pick daisies,
he is immediately called to order by invisible red flags that are
more imperative than any rocket signal.[1]

He can, of course, express doubts about the spirit of the Constitution, declare that he doesn't believe in God, wear suède
shoes,[2] sport a coloured shirt for dinner, and choose to live in a
'bad' quarter of town (one that is inhabited by, or is close to,
Puerto Ricans, Chinese and Negroes). But he will be written
off as a suspect soul, as an individual who perversely follows the
wrong road and should be avoided. As for his habitation, he
will be said, in the best railway style, to live 'on the wrong side
of the tracks'.[3]

After a few hours in New York, you are incorporated in the
railway schedule and become a part of the network. Con-
sciously or unconsciously you become yourself a little train,
heedful of the timetables and the switches. Take, for example,
the express-waiters of the restaurants and drug-stores.[4] The easy-
going European method generally employed by Sonia or

[1] It should be noted that the longing to pick daisies is quickly curbed by poison
ivy, a venomous plant growing all over the United States which provokes a
violent itch and an irritating rash.
[2] Major Thompson, who sometimes wears suède shoes, was one day asked by
a most polite young man if he was A.C. or D.C. These letters do not, as the Major
thought at first, designate a decoration, but are abbreviations for Alternating
Current and Direct Current. They refer to those homosexuals who are not afraid
of women. The Major, who doesn't care two hoots what others think of him,
went on wearing suède shoes in the U.S.A. whenever he felt like it.
[3] This often heard American expression originates from the fact that many
towns in the U.S.A. are divided by a railway line separating the 'residential'
quarter from the poor quarter inhabited by Negroes.
[4] I am not talking, of course, of those New York restaurants which are more
French than American, and where you have time to kill reflecting on what you
are going to eat. I am talking here of feeding-places.

Madame Pochet, to wit: 'I think I'll take a grapefruit and then a steak and then . . . No, on thinking it over, better give me some smoked salmon, oh! and . . . well no! . . . a grapefruit,' cannot be applied here without risking a catastrophe. The moment you begin enumerating 'a grapefruit, a steak,' the express-waiter charts your itinerary on his little green pad (in duplicate). If you change your mind halfway through, you will see his face darken and frown. He has to tear up his little slip, which is too bad.

It's the same story with those numerous specialists you have to deal with in the hotels. You can't just stop the first flunkey going by and give him your dirty laundry, your shoes, a pair of trousers to be pressed and a button to be sewn on again. I have seldom seen a face as put out as the chambermaid's (a 'general' from Ireland) when Pochet handed her a pair of shoes the first day in New York. You could have sworn she had never touched that kind of merchandise in her life. The valet, a distinguished-looking gentleman, considered the shoes in his turn without touching them, and then said to Pochet in a rather scornful tone:

'Call the barbershop.'

For a moment Pochet was left wondering if in the United States shoes are given shampoos. Calling up the barber about a pair of shoes may seem strange to a foreigner, but what seemed stranger still to the valet was that this ignorant foreigner, come from God knows where, should not know that the express shoe-shine boy is stationed at the barber's.

I

THE REALM OF WRAPPING PAPER

You might think that the 'land of high-tension men', as Daninos has just called it, was the fastest in the world, and many people have this idea of the United States. But I must state that it is at once true and false. It is sometimes the fastest, but often the slowest too—as in the case of the trains themselves and even more of the cars which, though made to go one hundred and twenty miles an hour, can rarely do more than sixty, because of the speed limits imposed. Pochet, who was delighted to get behind the steering wheel of his new de luxe model in New York, had to travel a distance equal to Paris–Timbuctu before he could find a State where he could do one hundred and ten, and by the time he had reached Nevada he had lost all appetite for it.

Really, the United States is a strange country where everything is made to go faster than anywhere else and where everything seems organized to go more slowly (the only thing that goes damnably fast is the dollar, which disappears from one's pocket at high velocity).

The almost incessant use of pencil and paper has something to do with this phenomenon of deceleration. The Americans, who have a reputation for being men-machines, spend a considerable part of their existence writing, even while driving. Various and sundry acts that elsewhere require nothing in writing, here have to be carefully committed to paper.

When I take a taxi in Paris, the driver may begin by making me get out because I am not going in his direction. But if he accepts me, the first thing he does is drive me to the desired address without further formality. In New York the first thing a taxi-driver does is take out a pencil and pad and note down the time, the place he picked me up, and the address I've given him.

Sometimes, to be sure, he writes this all down while driving, which adds a dash of excitement to it all. The bus drivers, too, go in for a strange kind of bookkeeping which the simple-minded foreigner has difficulty in discerning the need for.

Even in the restaurant cars you are required to write down your order on a pad (with carbon copy). The handwriting of Europeans being often illegible, Madame Pochet was obliged, while travelling on the 'City of Denver' (Union Pacific Railways), to ask for her steak in capital letters, which made her furious. It also gave her a chance to unleash an attack on American cooking.

'That they do not know how to season a salad is pardonable,' she said. 'But that they dare to call "French dressing" this mixture of cream, tomato and vinegar they decorate it with, *ça non !*' Pochet immediately chimed in to say that people who, thanks to their 'freezers', sometimes make a steak wait three months before eating it and drink *café au lait* with their oysters cannot be taken seriously. At which point a Negro waiter proudly opened a bottle of California wine, the label of which read: 'Special Red Sparkling Burgundy,' and underneath it: 'Beware of Imitations.' It was more than Pochet could stomach and he couldn't get down another bite.

Here in every field paper is King. The waiting-rooms, like the offices themselves, are strewn with memorandums, notepads, pencils. As soon as he has a spare moment in his office, between two memos dictated to his secretary, our friend Cyrus B. Lippcott loves, while talking or telephoning, to doodle away at little geometric designs (which he preserves because, as he explained to me, in case of a nervous breakdown or a simple check-up,[1] these squares and circles, being a pure emanation of the subconscious, will provide his psychoanalyst with precious clues).

Like all Americans Lippcott is a lover of paper. Were Mrs Lippcott to forget to put a box of Kleenex in the car—but how could she forget this sacrosanct tissue which serves at once as handkerchief, napkin and make-up remover?—he would be as

[1] A general verification of the organs which Americans undergo at regular intervals, and notably after a trip to the Old World, notorious breeding-ground for germs.

'WHY DO YOU SAY YOU'RE A FAILURE IN LIFE WHEN YOU CAN PAY MY
BILLS?'

unhappy as Pochet without his *Guide Michelin*.[1] One of the
things that most amazed Lippcott during his latest stay in Paris
was to see its inhabitants walking about with loaves of bread
under their arms—unwrapped, *without paper!* For an asepticized and microbe-haunted American such a thing is simply
unthinkable. In his bathroom at the Statler Hotel, in Washing-

[1] The first thing you notice on the rear seat of any American car is a blue Kleenex
box. If you don't see it, it's because the manufacturer has provided a Kleenex box
in the car's interior.

ton, D.C., Pochet was struck speechless with admiration, over the (paper) seat-cover in the W.C. (Will I be forgiven for speaking of such things? After all, it did not concern me.) 'This seat,' guaranteed the notice placed alongside of the reserve supply of seat-covers, 'is perfectly sterilized and untouched by human hand'.[1] Was it because of this admonition that the intimacy of the bathroom suddenly seemed to Pochet to have been invested with an unusual solemnity?

You can imagine the daily torture that a trip to Gaul represents for Lippcott. In his own country everything is wrapped up—the salt, the sugar, the meat, the bread, the fruit, the dishes and even, in tiny cellophane envelopes, the postage stamps which the stamp machine distributes between little strips of cardboard. In one of the hotels we stayed at the breakfast was delivered to us in a cardboard container, which was shoved through a hatchway in the door. Martine finds 'their' wrappings so wonderful that she claims she could spend hours admiring a package before opening it (annoying in the case of a breakfast). In the meantime the number of boxes she has already laid aside is so great that if it keeps up I shall leave here boxed and crated.

'No, but look, *chéri*, how it's all wrapped up!' she said to me on seeing my laundry come back to me at the hotel.

And true enough: my shirts were returned to me neatly buried in a blue carton enveloped in shiny white paper, swathed in tissue paper, beribboned in green paper bands, and stuffed with sheets of grey cardboard backing. The only annoying thing—due no doubt to an excess of starch—was that the shirts themselves were as stiff as boards.

The U.S.A. is the Kingdom of Package Appeal. On certain days, when it rains, Lippcott, with his plastic hat-cover, shoe-covers, trouser-covers and raincoat, seems to me perfectly packaged. And it's a fact that at nine o'clock of any morning in New York the men and women, looking cleaner and more neatly dressed than any Latins in their Sunday best, seem to have just stepped out of their boxes.

[1] The chambermaid herself avoids touching the seat with her fingers, merely changing the paper which carries the germs.

For these paper-lovers the crowning day of the week is, quite naturally, the Sabbath. That day Cyrus and his family literally disappear behind mountains of paper (for the family: 26 lb. of Sunday newspaper). So much so that when I turned up unexpectedly at their place a couple of Sundays ago, at first I couldn't see them at all. I keep wondering, indeed, if on Sundays it is the Americans that devour their papers or the papers that swallow them up.[1]

All this is disconcerting to Pochet. He had a prefabricated America in his head, and it was not at all the one he has had thrust before his eyes. Every Frenchman knows—as Pochet believed—that the average American is a man who:

(*a*) wakes up to soft music on top of a skyscraper, chews a first chewing-gum tablet, and has a brainwave while shaving;

(*b*) gets breakfast ready for the American Divinity—his wife—while barely having time to think of his own;

(*c*) rushes into an express-elevator and from there into his fluid-drive limousine;

(*d*) pursued by motorcycle cops, races a roaring train, speeds over the railway crossing first and reaches the Exchange Mortgage Company before his rival, Mac (in the train);

(*e*) climbs, by successive flights of stairs, all the echelons of the hierarchy, finally invading the scenic-view office of the Company President, to whom he unfolds his latest idea (his feet up on the desk) and from whom he immediately receives warm congratulations and the management of the factory;

(*f*) bolts his lunch in a drugstore;

(*g*) returning home in the evening, dog-tired but victorious, finds a note from the Divinity informing him that weary of always waiting for him, she has taken the plane for Reno and is demanding a divorce for 'mental cruelty';

(*h*) is ruined the next day by the crash of the Exchange Mortgage Company, but, ever smiling, starts again from scratch as a simple workman with Ford; the future is his.

[1] Be it noted, however, that in the land of paper, there is one thing you are never asked for: your papers. You can live and die in the United States without ever having to show your papers.

In fact, nothing of the sort occurs. Lippcott never chews gum (out of date, poor form) and never would he have the insane idea of racing through a red light.

Back in France Pochet had been told of ruthless gangsters and ill-bred boys; but he finds people obeying a ritual of politeness infinitely more rigorous than in any country in Europe, even mine.[1]

He had been told that the Americans were simple, frugal people. Yet the Lippcotts would think it an offence to offer him fruit for dessert. It has become almost impossible to get a car in only one colour in America, and Martine claims that they have lovely little dresses, but that they can't keep themselves from adding a little '*kiki, qui fiche tout parterre*'.[2]

Pochet was expecting to find feverish, hectic people ceaselessly running around. Instead, he finds citizens who have mastered the art of hurrying slowly, who never run (at the Douglas Factory in Los Angeles signboards recommend: *We are in a hurry: don't run*), and who take their time over thinking.

When I hear Pochet talking business with Americans, I have the impression that, starting out from Paris, he has already reached Marseilles while his opposite numbers are still at Fontainebleu. Strange, but perhaps explainable. I have always thought that certain Anglo-Saxons, and all Americans, had

---

[1] Nothing impresses Pochet more than to see thirty Americans packed in an elevator, simultaneously take off their hats, as though moved by a single spring, to salute the entrance of a girl on the twenty-fourth floor. But what intrigues him even more is the ritual of the dinner table and the mechanical ballet of knife and fork. For meat: (*a*) take the fork in the left hand and the knife in the right; (*b*) set down the knife on the edge of the plate and transfer the fork to the right hand, while the left hand goes under the table; jab and eat; (*c*) begin the same operation all over again for the next piece. . . . For Pochet, who couldn't tell you just where his knife and fork go when he is eating and who insists on guarding his plate to the left and the right of him with his two hands, this little game of cut-and-jab-and-jab-and-cut seems quite incompatible with the art of good eating. When he expressed his surprise at finding American men, and particularly American women, eating with their left arms under the table, the Major told him that this custom dated from the days of the pioneers, who had to keep one hand on their Colts while eating. During the war the secret agents of the O.S.S. had to be taught to get rid of this habit as quickly as possible before going off on missions into enemy country. (P. D.)

[2] 'A little doo-dah that ruins everything.'

stomachs in their heads. And if exchanges of ideas sometimes seem more laborious in America than in Europe, it's because, unless they are ideas of standard size, the registration of which is easy, all unusual ideas must be filtered, examined, assimilated.

This explains a certain slowness in the uptake. The stomach doesn't assimilate—a common enough phenomenon of cerebral constipation. However, from the moment the stomach assimilates, the American beats the record for the course. One American has understood, and 166 million Americans understand with him. Individually slow, the Americans are an overwhelming collective force that no nation in the world can compete with. It was exactly what happened during the war. It took the Americans some time to understand that they were involved in the thing, but once they did so the battle was won. The world, or at any rate that part of it that couldn't get used to looking under its bed for skeletons, could now sleep in peace.

COCKTAIL PARTY

THE Americans, who leave very little to chance ever since chance led to the discovery of their country, have in recent times perfected, among other things, a school for dogs and gramophone records for parakeets.

I won't say much about the School for Well-Brought-up Dogs, which is intended not only to train, and particularly to restrain dogs in polite society (innate qualities in the British dog, Major Thompson assures us), but also to teach them to walk in a straight line in the street (without tugging on the leash), to bark correctly, and to wear dinner jackets.[1] But I should like to say something, on the other hand, about the unsuspected advantages to be derived from gramophone records for parrots—advantages accruing not so much to the parrots themselves as to newcomers to the United States.

When Cyrus B. Lippcott told me that he trained his parrot, Jasper, with the aid of a record, I only half believed him, and I rushed over to a record shop on Broadway privately persuaded that they were going to laugh in my face. This the salesman did, not to tell me it was a joke, but because my request seemed to

[1] It should be noted that in treeless cities the education of dogs must be particularly thorough. The school year for dogs corresponds to that of children (October–May). At the end of a six-month 'obedience class' the good pupil receives a diploma complete with gold seal and red ribbon. The unsatisfactory ones are sent out of the city and entrusted to friends in the country. The dinner jacket is only one of the many items in the wardrobe of the fashionable Yankee dog, which also includes camel-hair coats, charming little caps, and brightly coloured raincoats. It should be added that the standard of (dog) living is very high in New York, where a prize (*Prix du Chien*) is offered annually for the Most Elegant Dog, where dogs are fed on scientific diets, have their own bar (in marble) on Fifth Avenue (corner of Forty-sixth Street), their own visiting cards, their own hairdressers, and where you will look in vain for one of those unkempt mongrels with no fixed address.

him as preposterous as if I had asked for a concerto for piano and orchestra without naming the composer.

'There are twenty-five of them,' he said to me. 'Which do you want?'

To save face I pretended to choose one from the pile of records he brought me. Since then I have gone more deeply into the matter. Where there's smoke there's sure to be fire. If so many parrot records exist, it must be because there's a lot of parroting in the New York air.

I have always been struck by the way the parrot side of my nature develops as soon as I spend a few days in the United States. By dint of hearing the same formulas repeated morning, noon and night, one ends up unconsciously using them oneself. What are these formulas? To reply to this question I spent a whole day going around with a pocket tape-recorder (of which there are many models in the U.S.A.). In the evening I added up the most frequently recorded expressions. Without mentioning the incessant 'Glad to meet yous', 'Hope to see you agains', I cannot, for reasons of space, make a complete list here of the fifty-odd formulas that enable one to get along in the United States (*lovely, darling, relax, check! Nuts! O.K. wonderful! fine, efficient, fabulous, gorgeous* being among the most used).[1]

How then is one to go about memorizing and correctly pronouncing this pocket vocabulary?

Cyrus Lippcott put me on the right track by recommending the one used by parrots. What a heap of time you save by this method! If you tried to collect the innumerable formulas of the American language all by yourself, you would lose precious hours and risk many lapses of memory. The parrot record, on the other hand, faithfully reproduces all the key phrases, murmured ten times over by a charming feminine voice, suave but well articulated. Besides, a parrot's education is a thousand times more rapid than a schoolboy's. A parrot must be very quick in the uptake and ready to conform to the prevailing usages from

[1] The Americans are the greatest consumers of formulas in the world. They speak in formulas, eat formulas, write formula-letters from abroad (Formula No. 1: 'Wish you were here!') and send you happy birthday greetings with Western Union's Telegraphic Formula No. 4.

JACKET COVER FOR A RECORDING OF 'ROMANTIC PHRASES' DESTINED
TO EDUCATE PARROTS, BUT WHICH THE AUTHOR USED FOR HIS OWN
EDUCATION

the start, so as not to say just any old thing when in society.
There's no point wasting years teaching him the reactions of
sunflowers or the role of Pericles in antiquity. He can be taught
what to say in a living-room in the very first record-class (*social
contacts*).

That is why, having become a parrot myself, I learned more
in one lesson (under the direction of Allen B. Jacobs—78 revolu-

tions) than in a month of tape-recordings. And at the beginning
of the Second Year Class, suitable for a parrot of forty-three—
my age—I had already reached the *Romantic Vocabulary*, with
phrases like: *Hi babe!* [1] *Hello sweetheart!*, *Gosh! You're cute!*,
How about a date?

At the end of eight days' training, I was ready for anything.
Ready to go about without danger in the American world.
Ready, above all, to face that redoubtable institution: the cocktail party. For the descendants of those colonists who craved
solitude and the wide open spaces, who crossed an ocean to free
themselves from the pomp and circumstance of the Old World,
now feel a daily need to crowd themselves into overheated rooms
where, unable to breathe or to hear each other, they make a
ceremonial sacrifice to the most sacred of all rites in the United
States: the cocktail.

The American cocktail is organized in honour of anyone and
anything: a reception for a duchess, the arrival of a writer, the
visit of a cousin from Detroit. It allows you to meet a great
number of people with whom it is quite naturally impossible to
talk, but with whom you can make a date for some other day.
On that day your new acquaintance, who would think it dis-
obliging to receive you alone, will invite in a few friends in your
honour and make it a 'party'. This is a vicious circle from which
no one seems anxious to escape.

Somewhat similar to the Parisian cocktail party, though
infinitely more frequent, more ritualistic and more formal, the
American cocktail party is utterly unlike the London variety:
one more difference between these two countries. English life is
nothing but a huge masquerade ball in which the participants
contrive to hide from you their feelings, their street numbers,
their hobbies, their incomes, their decorations, their sorrows,
their talents, their achievements and even their names. (It's

[1] Masters in the art of decontraction, Americans are also unsurpassed in matters
of contraction. *Hi!* is the final contraction of 'How are you?', which became
Hi-ya, before being finally reduced to two letters. Like the schoolboys in France,
Americans love to shorten words and, above all, names. In a country where
Dwight D. Eisenhower becomes 'Ike', Stevenson 'Steve' and Cyrus B. Lippcott
'Cy', Montesquieu would become 'Monti' or 'T.Q.'

THE MAJOR AT AN AMERICAN COCKTAIL PARTY

almost impossible to know just whom it is you are talking to at
a London cocktail party.)

America, on the other hand, is a huge glasshouse where everything is advertised in black and white: success, financial status,
hobbies and, above all, names. Our friend Cyrus revels in those
conventions,[1] at which he prances around like a child at a summer
camp, with his name (and State) in his buttonhole. Not here
would Pochet risk describing his ascent of the Puy de Dôme to
an old Everest hand. Besides, to avoid all error, it is quite common for the hostess to preface her introduction with a few vital
statistics: 'Allow me to introduce the well-known champion who
ran the two twenty (yards) in twenty and two-tenths seconds,
Mr Melvin Sam Holgerson.'

And now here is the (high fidelity) pocket tape-recording of a
cocktail party held at 696 Fifth Avenue, New York, between
5.30 and 7 p.m. There were, as you will notice, a few French
people in the room to add to the confusion:

'Glad to meet you! ... Isn't that cute! ... Yes, but watch
out: New York isn't America. ... You should go out West. ...
May I introduce Mr Thaddeus Apfelbaum, of Apfelbaum,
Birbenstock and Company. ... Pleased to meet you! ... If
you go to Los Angeles, don't fail to look up the DeWitte Clintons, they're delightful people and they know everybody; I'll
give you a note for them. ... Hope to see you again. ... *Ce
n'est pas un pays; c'est un continent; prenez leurs trains, eh bien
vous passez la journée dans le train, vous êtes aux États Unis. Vous
passez la nuit, vous êtes encore aux États Unis. Vous repassez la
journée, vous êtes toujours* ...[2] Hi babe! Well, I'll tell you now:
in three years it'll be all over; she did that purely for ambition's
sake. ... They're a bunch of snobs! ... Let me introduce Mrs
Mildred McPherson, of the Columbia Broadcasting System. ...
Don't you think there's a touch of Farouk in him? ... If you

[1] Monster rallies, all over the U.S.A., to bring together in one or more hotels
of the same city members of an Association, party or corporation.
[2] 'It's not a country; it's a continent. Take their trains, well, you spend the day
in the train, and you're in the United States. You spend the night, and you're
still in the United States. You spend another day, and you're still. ...'

go to Chicago, don't fail to look up the Fergusons; they'll give
you a royal welcome and they know everybody. I'm going to
give you a note. . . . *Non, ils ne sont pas bêtes; ce sont de grands
enfants.* . . . *Vous avez beau dire, nous pourrions prendre modèle sur
eux pour beaucoup de choses, tenez leurs douches par exemple, eh
bien, ce matin, vous ne le croirez pas, Alfred.* . . .[1] You're welcome! . . . And the Negroes? Have you ever thought seriously
about the Negro problem? . . . Well, I don't find her so cute, so
there. . . . It'll last six months. . . . You must go to Las Vegas!
. . . You know what I'd do if I were you? I'd hire a car. . . .
Glad to meet you! . . . I love black children, I find them little
darlings. . . . If you were American, you'd speak differently. . . .
You know she comes from a very good family, her mother's a
Cabot. . . . Hi! Paree, ah! Paree! Lovely city! *Oui, mais
Mendès n'a pas voulu, voilà*[2] . . . You should go to San Francisco.
. . . Relax! . . . I thought they were divorced? . . . If I were in
your place, I'd take a bus, there you can really talk to people. . . .
Gorgeous! . . . I thought they were in Mexico. . . . I give them
just six months. . . . I never would've believed it of her. . . .
Come back in a year's time and we'll talk it over again. . . .
Check! . . . D'you realize you're on the same latitude as
Madrid? . . . *Mais voyons! Ils sont bien plus près des Russes que
vous ne le pensez.* . . .[3] If you haven't seen Kansas City, you
haven't seen anything. . . . I picked this up this morning at
Saks: two dollars and fifty cents, how d'you like that? . . . The
Chinese won't co-operate, you'll see. . . . Pleased to meet you.
. . . Is it really true that France has gone Communist? . . . What
about a date? *Au fond, c'est très province, quoi?* Communist? . . .
*Mais New York, ma chère, c'est Angoulême, vous verrez: AN-
GOULÊME! Leurs robes du soir sont d'un kiki!* . . . *Oui, mais
ils font de gentilles robes de sport.* . . .[4] Bulganin will never make

[1] 'No, they aren't stupid; they are just big children. . . . It's all very well your
saying we could follow their example for many things. Take their showers, for
example, well, this morning, would you believe it, Alfred. . . .'
[2] 'Yes, but Mendès (-France) didn't want to, so there.'
[3] 'But of course! They're much closer to the Russians than you think. . . .'
[4] 'Basically, it's provincial, what? But New York, my dear, is like Angoulême, you'll see; ANGOULÊME! . . . Their evening gowns are really something! . . . Yes, but they make nice sport dresses. . . .'

it. . . . They're very strong. . . . They told me it stank. . . .
Have you seen this new U-bomb? . . . She's perfect, but I liked
her better in *Cute Lady*. . . . To really get to know them, you
have to live in the Middle West. . . . You should go to Okla-
homa. . . . No, to Sioux City! Yessir, Sioux City! *Ils vont voir
le psychoanalyste pour un oui ou pour un non*. . . . *Les enfants sont
rois*. . . .[1] It's better in orlon. . . . If you go to Seattle, I'll give
you a note for the Chandler-Lewises; they know everybody and
with them. . . . When you're face to face with a mass of three
hundred million people. . . . If you haven't seen Dallas, you
haven't seen anything. . . . They arrived yesterday. . . . The
Duke is here. . . . They left this morning. . . . *Ce que je trouve
épatant c'est leurs ice-creams! Vous savez qu'ils font du vin?* . . .
On aura tout bu![2] . . . He's with his wife? . . . We're going tomorrow. . . . How long are you staying? . . . If you go to
Kansas City, be sure to look up Collidge Junior, the old man has
gone to pot, it's the nephew who runs the show. . . . But take
the train, and be done with it. . . . The nice thing about it is that
you don't even have to wipe the dishes. . . . I won't give them
six months to get divorced. . . . She killed him all right. . . . A
word of advice: take the plane. . . .'

When I was alone again in the street, my befuddled brain was
a heaving mass of faces, formulas and notions clashing together
in an infernal kaleidoscope. The Major had disappeared. The
Pochets had gone off to the Lippcotts. It was raining. I suddenly felt very much alone, as one can only be in a city of eight
million isolated souls that 800 parties have momentarily brought
together. The bus or the train? Sioux City or Baltimore? I had
to look up the DeWitte Clintons, and the MacClutches, and the
Pattersons. . . .

What was I to do? Assuming I could find those hastily
scribbled down names. Ah, names! I have never had much luck

---

[1] 'They go to see the psychoanalyst for a Yes or a No. . . . The children are
rulers. . . .'
[2] 'The thing I find great is their ice-cream! . . . You know they make wine? . . .
We'll have drunk everything! . . .'

with names. If I go to Los Angeles, pinning all my hopes on the DeWitte Clintons, I'm sure to discover on getting there that the DeWitte Clintons aren't *it* at all . . . it's the Ashburns I should have got in touch with!

When someone says to me: 'If you visit the Chrysler Plant in Detroit, look up Bill Richardson. He's the boss's right-hand man. Has everyone eating out of his hand', I discover when I get there that the boss lost his right hand two years ago. The gateman even has trouble finding the name in the personnel list.

'You say Bill Richardson?'

It obviously doesn't ring a bell. . . . But hold on, here he is, after all!

'RICHARDSON (Bill) . . . He runs the presswork branch. Out here, first on your left and then bear right. . . .'

Gosh! Whadda ya know? Nuts!

THE ART OF SLEEPING WITH YOUR EYES OPEN

THE most painful thing in life is not being bored. It's being compelled to pretend you're having a good time.

Take those dinner parties—those terrible dinner parties where you must talk, where you must scintillate. Where you must know who's who, what to say to whom, how to reply to what. On top of a glass is a little card on which you try to decipher the name of—Wanamaker-Baxter. You say to yourself: That's petroleum . . . and it turns out to be public utilities. You have to start all over again. Ah! Those dinners where you must give your opinion on the Pentagon, Eisenhower, Poujade, Suez and China!

What can one do about it?

Well, the Americans have given me the answer to the problem. In a country where the man who can't live in public is banned by society, it was only normal that they should one day discover a way of allowing people to sleep upright while appearing wide awake.

Long experience has taught me that boredom begins with the feet. When you're gay, when you're relaxed, you don't think of your feet. You put them anywhere, any old how. You can even scratch them. It's marvellous! But at dinner parties, or at any rate those that I am thinking of here, your feet are the first to start swelling with boredom. By a kind of parallel, though somewhat higher, action your back begins to sag, your head begins to nod, your eyelids droop. Deafened by the uproar, by the noise of dishes and the dishing out of noise, 'You're not taking a second helping? It's all there is . . .', harassed by shrill 'Have you been going out a lot lately? . . . And the ski-ing? . . .'

you feel an invincible torpor steal over you, and in the semi-consciousness you softly settle into your dream of that distant land, so close but inaccessible, that El Dorado from which ties are banished and where you can walk barefoot on the carpet and bury your nose in a sofa—home. Oh! at nine o'clock in the evening how far away one o'clock in the morning so often seems! You will have to cross the Urals, span Siberia, argue with Mao Tse-Tung, give your opinion on Prince Rainier, and lose yourself in a labyrinth of liaisons. . . .

Not long ago at a dinner in Washington a gentleman was explaining how twenty years ago he had bought a stick of barley sugar from Grace Kelly on the beach at Atlantic City. I could have done with a bit of it myself, but my neighbour had me backed up against Greenland. 'Do you really think one can put up with a thing like that?' he asked me. 'Of course not!' I said. 'It's the same with Madagascar,' he resumed, and, far from Grace Kelly, I had to catch up at Tananarive.

Until recently—that is before receiving Cyrus B. Lippcott's advice—I used to employ a pretty primitive method, effective but sometimes dangerous. You let yourself, bit by bit, be bemused by your neighbour. Why talk? He talks about everything so well! Yes, as you've guessed, he's one of those staggering men who go from Montherlant to Mollet by way of the White House, with a passing reference or two to NATO and UNESCO. There's only one thing to do with this kind of man—as with a watch, wind him up again, the most convenient winding-up-again words being: 'You're dead right!' or else 'Oh, absolutely!' A 'You really think so?', a simple 'Oh, come now!', an 'In my opinion, it's unlikely' can also set the convoy going again. If you want to hedge a little, an 'I don't think I'd go quite as far as that, but . . .' can be risky, whereas a simple 'Oh! but how true!' will put this human locomotive at his ease and set him off again. You can eat your chicken in peace.

There's only one trouble with this method: you suddenly notice that something is wrong. The train has stopped. You realize that a question has been put to you and that it's not just a grunt of agreement, but a precise answer that is expected of you.

You have just said: 'In my opinion, it's unlikely', thinking that you have fallen in with the drift of your neighbour's conversation, and only too late you realize that he asked you if you were a bachelor. It's embarrassing.

This kind of catastrophe used to befall me all the more frequently at the start of my trip to the United States, thanks to the increased incomprehensibility of the cacophonic babble I was subjected to. At a dinner in Boston, where I had done quite a bit of mileage on 'Yes and Nos' and 'No doubts', I had just come out with an emphatic 'I never would have thought it!' when I perceived that I had been asked if I was born in Paris. I was finished!

It was after this misadventure that Cyrus Lippcott, to whom I had confided it, recommended the use of some miraculous glasses that keep you from ever giving others the impression you're bored. These glasses, called Refuge-Specs, patented and manufactured by the H. Gardner Company of Ossining (N.Y.) were destined to change my life. With them there is no need to say a single word, so much do they give your partner the impression that you are drinking in his words. You can simply go to sleep while seeming to be the most captivated person in the world.

These glasses, as you may have guessed, have eyes of their own, eyes painted on them with eyelids and eyebrows, which it would be an understatement to describe as matching reality, inasmuch as they far surpass it. Two tiny holes pierced at the level of your pupils allow you from time to time to cast a real glance at the situation. ('Nap politely yet look alert, at the Opera, at conferences, or dinner parties.') You can, of course, yourself choose the model you like and which will best match your complexion. 'Select the suitable personality', says the explanatory notice, which establishes three 'basic personalities':

(*a*) Cool, intellectual, (*b*) Eager beaver, (*c*) Shy, demure.

Each of the three models has its particular advantages. To sleep politely at the theatre or during conferences, I would particularly recommend the 'cool, intellectual' model. On the other hand, the 'Eager beaver'—two wide-open and knowledge-hungry eyes—allowed me cheerfully to survive a lengthy harangue on the International Monetary Fund that would, in any other circumstances, have completely ossified me. In my opinion, the best solution is to arm yourself with all three pairs at once, since your partner may be surprised to be confronted by such a fixed stare for long periods of time. All you have to do is to take advantage of one of those moments when men take off their glasses to rub their eyelids (a gesture well thought of among big industrialists, businessmen, and even intellectuals) and with a negligent gesture exchange an *Eager beaver* for a *Shy, demure*.

These 'wide-open eye' spectacles are, when all is said and done, just one of the 1001 replies to the 'Hows' that American experts keep filling the bookstores with—from *How to make friends* and *How to live with yourself* to *How to buy and sell* and *How to win your wife's confidence*.

There is not a 'How' that escapes the sagacity of these experts. The spectacular reply to the question *How to sleep while seeming awake?* only goes to prove that in a country where everything is done to provide amusement, there's sometimes a touch of boredom in the air. You have only to spend a few days in a typically American small town like Decatur (Alabama), which is strangely like Du Quoin (Illinois) or Cœur d'Alene (Idaho)—with its Main Street, its First National Bank (neo-Greek façade), its little brick schoolhouse, its Ladies' Club, its Liggett's Drug Store, its town hall, its supermarket and its Methodist tabernacle, to realize that life in the U.S.A. is not always a picnic. This explains in part the success of lectures in this country—particularly foreign lectures, the word of a visitor from afar always being invested with a special prestige. If a Norwegian, or an Englishman, or a Frenchman turns up one night in Des Moines (Iowa), he is sure to pack the house. Whether he is an explorer, missionary, industrialist, deep-sea diver, writer, or cyclist, he represents for the local Ladies' Club a topic of conversation, an excuse for going out, an alternative to TV or the radio.

The subject matters very little, as is proved by this authentic story. One of Major Thompson's fellow countrymen was some years ago vegetating in the United States, whither the hazards of existence had brought him. Like many men he was casting around for an idea that would bring him success. One day a certain Colonel Bodley (another of the Major's countrymen, and like him an ex-Indian Army officer, now living near Boston) advised his compatriot, who had a certain gift of speech, to take up lecturing.

'All right. But what about?'

'Any old thing,' cried the Colonel. And then, as they were going past a church, he said: 'Here, why don't you talk about bells?'

'Bells? But—I don't know a blessed thing about bells!'

'More's the reason! Mug up on the subject and then tell us what you've learned.'

The Colonel's friend followed his advice and plunged into the *Encyclopaedia Britannica*. After one hour he already knew more about bells than you, I or any American. He quickly realized that there was a tremendous amount to be said about bells, bell-ringers, handbells and belfries, from the first Chinese bell to Big Ben, via jingle-bells, Canterbury bells, bluebells, dumb-bells and *Les Cloches de Corneville*. Today he could write a 'How' book entitled, *How to succeed in life thanks to bells*. For it's thanks to bells that this man is now making a small fortune in the U.S.A. With his one lecture, for which he was at first paid $15, but for which he now gets $300, he goes from town to town, year in year out, earning a good $10,000 a year—which for bells isn't bad.

It should be noted that bells in themselves present certain advantages. They notably allow you to make a personal allusion to the bell of the locality you are speaking in, for there is always at least one bell in a village, even if it's only the bell of a passing train.

'It gives me particular pleasure,' the lecturer assures his audience, 'to speak to you tonight about bells, for your church (or town hall or fire engine) bell has a quite unique ring. . . .'

At one blow he has won the sympathy of the ladies of the Women's Club, who form the backbone of American audiences and are ever avid to learn something about anything. I can't guarantee, of course, that the audience won't contain a few recalcitrant husbands who, having been dragged along by their wives, will pull out their famous Refuge-Specs but no matter! For at least eight days in Pascagoula (Mississippi) they'll be talking about bells. It makes, shall we say, a 'nice conversation piece'?

xvii

AMERICA IN A NUTSHELL

 When I came back to Paris from the United States, I told my editor: 'All things considered, I think I could sum up America in a phrase.'

Notwithstanding the importance of this announcement, he did not look at all happy. Brevity may be a salutary virtue, but the writer who returns from a 15,000-mile trip to tell his literary sponsor that he can write it all up in three lines is regarded with a jaundiced eye. And even though I had to travel all the way to Salt Lake City (Utah)—that is, a good 6000 miles from Paris—to pick up this phrase, it seemed really too expensive to my editor. 'You can't do this to me,' he said. 'Better go back there.'

I therefore reimbursed my publishers by forking out something like 80,000 extra words, but my opinion hasn't changed for all that. All America is still summed up for me in the phrase I heard one morning at the Utah Hotel in Salt Lake City. I had asked to be called at 7 a.m. At the stated hour the telephone rang. And over the wire came the divine voice of the American telephone girl, a voice formed at the Voice School before the mirror of amiability (three months for a degree), a voice full of sex appeal, sweetness and precision:

'Good morning, Mr Denainos! It's seven o'clock! I hope you enjoyed your sleep! Weather is nice and temperature thirty-six degrees Fahrenheit. Thank you!'

These twenty-two words are America in a nutshell. First of all, my name! Oh, adorable switchboard operator, how well you learned to say my name! Up there in that anonymous room on the fourteenth floor of an American hotel, where I was alone with a black Bible, the telephone directory and the distant wailing of the locomotives of the Western Pacific, your beautifully modulated voice came through the hopeless dawn, leaving a trail of bell-like echoes ringing in my ears: '. . . ning! . . . nos! . . . clock! . . . joy! . . . nice! . . . kyou!' You spoke the same words to Monsieur Pochet, and he too no longer felt alone in the land of the Mormons. Welcoming America greeted him through your voice: she graciously invited him to get up and live.

'Good morning, Mr Pochett!'

That morning, amid 166 million souls, in this nation of pioneer conquests and struggles for existence, you gave him strength by uttering his name. In Salt Lake City Pochet is not just anybody; he's Monsieur Pochet, and you know that he's French, that he likes Chateaubriants and the Folies Bergère, that he has the *Légion d'Honneur* and a bit of the Eiffel Tower in him.

Americans cultivate names as we Frenchmen cultivate potatoes. No sooner does Pochet arrive at a hotel and register, than the manager, who can read upside down, catches his name—this name that will never leave him: 'Good morning, Mister Pochett. . . . You're welcome, Mister Pochett!' He could just as well be called Mavrogordato or De Stumpf-Quichelier; the reaction would be the same. Americans are name-catchers, and those whose job it is to specialize in public relations possess a particular aptitude for this kind of sport. They catch the most forbidding name with the agility of a butterfly-collector, promptly pinion it, mount it, offer it back, preserved and framed, as though it were one of their most cherished specimens.[1]

One of the great teachers of the American way of life, Mr Dale Carnegie, lays due stress on the importance of names in his book, *How to Win Friends and Influence People*. He cites the revealing cases of people who have succeeded in life simply because they could pronounce names pleasantly, with a smile, thus creating a climate of confidence.

In the plane the T.W.A. air hostess, who has fifty-seven passengers to take care of, asks Monsieur Pochet—whom she

[1] In America government buildings, banks, railway stations, steamship companies and even the elevators of large stores carry leather or brass plaques, with the employee's name on it. When you apply for a ticket to Miami at Pan American Airways, you don't address yourself just to anybody, but to Mr A. S. Pegram, and at the post office it's Mr J. H. Murchison who gives you a fifteen-cent stamp.

PSYCHOPANORAMA

L AMERICAN TOWN

didn't know ten minutes earlier and whom she may never see again in her life: 'Would you like some coffee, Mr Potchett?' In so doing, she gives him the comforting sensation of remaining Monsieur Pochet, even 18,000 feet above Death Valley and lost in the immensity of a continent where barely a hundred years ago the dog-eating Redskins smoked their peace pipes by the bodies of their scalped victims. She caresses him with the soft name of Potchett, she extracts him in two syllables from the abyss of anonymity, she gives him a gentle push along the road to fame.

This no doubt is why I find the United States rather hell, for the first thing you must do here is remember the names of the people you are introduced to, and there is nothing I forget more easily—unless it's the names of people I already know, and even my own.

'I hope you enjoyed your sleep.'

Oh, telephone girl of my dreams, how sweet is your voice when it says 'enjoy'! Lovely voice. . . . I would almost ask you to come on up, but no! that wouldn't be proper, that wouldn't be American. Yes, I enjoyed my sleep. Here people *enjoy* everything—a good night's sleep, a good outing, a good whisky, a good vacation, a good party, a good bed.[1] Your solicitude touches me. You are the voice of America, the voice of this Realm of Friendliness, where all day long the air rings with 'Glad to meet you' and 'You're welcome'.

All over the world, of course, people tell you they are very happy to meet you. But Americans really seem to be so. When we French say '*très heureux*', we might just as well say '*condoléances*' or '*A Bientôt*'.[2] We never think for a moment of being happy, for we already know enough people as it is. But in the United States it's just the opposite. People are delighted to get to know you, and they seem to have been waiting for this blessed moment for the last ten years. Two bright eyes plunge into

[1] A pamphlet that was put out during the war for the benefit of the members of the Women's Army Corps advised them, when importuned in enemy or occupied territory by over-enterprising men: 'If things become too difficult just relax and enjoy yourself!'

[2] French for 'So long'.

yours, a smile lights up the face of the newcomer, and a hearty handshake seals the exalted moment: 'Glad to meet you!'

All must share this spirit of general affability. It's being un-American to pull a long face, not to smile at the new day, at the person you meet, at the task awaiting you. Everywhere posters remind you: 'Keep smiling!' [1] You are required to keep smiling all your life, right up to your last gasp—and even after it, since post mortem make-up artists undertake, by an ultimate contraction of the zygomatic muscles, to fix it for eternity. The poorly trained foreigner sometimes succumbs beneath this avalanche of friendliness. And it is also true that in this game of smiles and affability American men wear themselves out faster than women.

'The whole question,' Major Thompson said to me, 'boils down to deciding whether it's better to live to a ripe old age among disagreeable people or to die young among the most welcoming people in the world.'

Death is not a more pleasant prospect in the U.S.A. than elsewhere, but it is so much better presented.

'. . . and temperature is thirty-six degrees Fahrenheit. Thank you!'

This was perhaps what most amazed Pochet. For a fleeting moment he must have imagined the look on the night porter's face at the Hôtel de la Gare at Poitiers if asked to wake him up in the morning with a question about his sleep and a report on the temperature outside. Here in the United States they not only ask nothing of you, but they give you everything, adding a 'Thank you!' at the end. [2]

---

[1] Even American dogs are not exempted from this obligation. A couple of pills, a new product made for the canine world, are guaranteed within forty-eight hours to bring a smile to the surliest bulldog. For further details, consult the dog psychiatrist in your neighbourhood.

[2] This 'thank you', pronounced with a markedly rising inflection by American feminine voices, is used on all sorts of occasions, and even when there is no need to say 'thank you' at all. It can sometimes be disconcerting. When you tell a Frenchwoman that she has the loveliest eyes in the world, she smiles, says nothing or else: '*Vous êtes fou!*' (You're mad!), and occasionally lets herself be kissed. When you tell an Englishwoman that she has the loveliest eyes in the world, she stops you, saying: 'Don't be silly!' When you tell an American woman that she has the loveliest eyes in the world, she says: 'Thank you', as though you had just

And what precision! The voice did not say: 'There's a nip in the air!' or 'It's chilly out, be sure to dress warmly.' No, it said: thirty-six degrees Fahrenheit. In America a sentence isn't really a sentence unless there's at least one figure in it.

Monsieur Pochet is a grown boy: he knows what he must do when the thermometer reads 36 degrees Fahrenheit if he isn't to bring a sore throat back to Madame, thanks!

'Thank you very much!' he himself replied to the switch-board operator, already feeling himself to be part of this land of courteous service, where even the cigarette machines are made to say 'thank you'. 'Thanks for buying me,' says the chocolate bar wrapper. 'Thanks' says the voice of the new robot in United States post offices when you buy a stamp off him.

The American 'thank you' is not just a word; it can also become a function. What are you? 'I am a thanker.' In the U.S.A. there are 'thankers' whose job it is to thank others. During the war, when blood donors used to line up at Red Cross plasma centres, they would be met at the exit by a lady thanker, a lady with a monthly remunerated smile who thanked them for co-operating in the war effort. They had smilingly obeyed the Number 1 law of America—co-operation.

---

passed her the salt. Things stay where they are until the next move is made; it's the rule of the game. I may add that she will say 'thank you' in exactly the same tone for 'Your dress is lovely' as for 'I like your handwriting'.

THE PRAYING MANTIS

(or 'The Secret of American Womanhood')

(*Major Thompson having expressed a desire to say a few words about American women, doubtless because he feared I might treat the subject properly, I gladly yield the pen to him once again.
—P. D.*)

I already know what my good friend Daninos is going to say; he is going to say that I care more about animals than about human beings, and it's true of course that, as a good Englishman, I'm more attached to the first than the second. But good heavens! Is it my fault if I have probed the secret of American womanhood by way of the American heifer? And can I honestly be blamed for being so struck, not to say shocked, by the American woman's omnipotence that I have come to liken her to a praying mantis who devours three or four husbands in a lifetime and replenishes herself on insurance policies and alimonies?

I shall, no doubt, be accused of being prone to exaggeration in this field, since I belong to a nation where man is king. But even Pochet is of much the same opinion. One hundred years ago the United States seemed to be a land of widowers; today it seems to him the greatest boarding-house for widows in the world. He can't get over meeting so many women who speak gaily of their third or fourth husbands.

One day when he was visiting a famous Fifth Avenue jewellery store in search of a *petit quelque chose* for his wife to mark the trip by, the salesman said to Pochet:

'We never ask a customer "How is your husband?" He's sure to be either dead or divorced. Besides, we never have men coming into our store; it's the women who do all the buying.

The kind of slick seducer who orders a diamond clip to be delivered to Baroness So-and-So in the hope of obtaining her favours is a strictly Latin type; here people want to play it safe.'

As far as I'm concerned, my mind is made up. Not only do American men use up a shocking amount of their strength in work, mostly to assure the well-being of the voracious mantis, but the latter holds them in a state closely akin to slavery. Just take poor old Cyrus B. Lippcott. From the moment he gets up to prepare breakfast for his Divinity right up to the moment he goes to bed at night, after absorbing the TV programme his wife has chosen, he hardly has an instant of peace and quiet. He has only to buy the latest model refrigerator or the latest 'Hi-Fi' record-player for his wife to start talking of the even more up-to-date ones the Fergusons have. And here is the poor fellow with another complex!

On the boat, coming back from their vacation in Europe, Mrs Lippcott was already telling Cyrus of her plans for 'doing' the Caribbean next year. Add to this the fact that most American wives keep complaining that their husbands come home exhausted from the office and think only of going to bed, instead of wanting to 'go places and do something'. Really, these wives have deplorable habits. They ought to be disciplined!

For that I suppose we shall have to wait a goodish time. In the meantime, I don't suppose I've ever seen anyone look more startled than the after-dinner company of one of those venerable Beacon Street houses in Boston. And all because, as I was settling into a comfortable armchair, I asked Martine if she'd mind fetching my pipe, which I had left in my raincoat. Mrs O'Neil, our Boston hostess, couldn't believe her ears, nor could Mrs Bainbridge, or the Cabots, her guests. Why, the idea of it! Fancy asking your wife to leave the drawing-room and fetch your pipe! An unheard-of enormity in the United States, even in the most English of cities. And to think that Martine complied with a smile! That was the last straw. I had stood the world on its head!

Even Pochet has been bothered by all this, though he may by

MAJOR THOMPSON, FOLLOWED BY MRS BRUCE PATTERSON, SURPRISES HIS
OLD COMRADE-IN-ARMS, 'THE WOLF OF THE ARDENNES' (COLONEL BRUCE
PATTERSON), NOW RESTORED TO THE JOYS OF DOMESTIC LIFE

now have grown accustomed to the manners of a country where man anticipates a woman's slightest wish. There's something automatic and ritualistic about the way American men get up the moment a woman walks in or out of a drawing-room, the way they help a lady into her chair at the dinner table, and the way they rush to carry their companion's coat, bags, packages and umbrella as soon as, and often before, she shows the slightest sign of fatigue.

By jove! I don't call it politeness. I call it obedience. Never would an Englishman think of being reduced to the status of footman.

Madame Pochet, however, finds this a blissful state of affairs:

'They are *so* much more polite than our men, *n'est-ce pas?*' she said to Martine, who, of course, agreed.

I must say that Pochet has never been more attentive than since his sojourn in the United States. He never drives anywhere to pick up his wife now without also getting out to open the door for her. And he always thinks of the little push to be given her chair when she sits down at table.

'*On m'a changé mon Alfred!*' she says.

Well, Pochet can be changed. But not I!

Now my touchy friend Daninos has objected that women all over the world have a touch of the praying mantis in them. He has also pointed out that the conditions of work in the United States are better than anywhere else. All this perplexed me to the point of wondering if I were not barking up the wrong tree. Still, there was one fact no one could deny: in this hemisphere, between the 25 degrees and the 49 degrees latitude, man wears himself out much more quickly than woman. Was the answer to this damnable riddle to be looked for, then, in purely geographic causes?

Well, it was finally an Iowa cattle raiser, a Mr Clarence McKinley, who let me in on the secret while I was visiting his ranch near Council Bluffs. I am a trifle embarrassed at having to divulge this secret to the general public, but I feel duty bound to do so.

I know that highly responsible experts have made valuable

'LOOK HARRY, WHAT A DISGRACE, TREATING A WOMAN LIKE THAT!
IT'S HIGH TIME WE STARTED CIVILIZING THESE PEOPLE!'

statistical studies of the behaviour of the American male, and yet I think I have gone almost as far as they through a study of the American cow.[1] Clarence McKinley offered me the proof: whereas female cattle, and in general all domestic female animals imported into the United States,[2] develop with growing strength, the males begin to wilt after a few years and rapidly lose their reproductive powers. Breeders of thoroughbreds and pedigree cattle must therefore frequently replenish their stock of stallions and bulls (particularly, I feel bound to add, with Aberdeen Anguses, Durhams and Guernseys! I can already hear Daninos exclaiming that I am 'not half' proud of the supremacy of these splendid British beasts).

Be that as it may, it seems that this physical law applies with equal rigour to American men. Whereas the hen-pecked male is finally eliminated in the quarter-finals, the female reaches the finals more robust than ever. She wields authority with masculine dynamism and becomes ever more avid for action, reforms, parties, discussions, trips. The twenties are the age of glamour and cover-girls, and if one only read the popular magazines one might end up wondering if there are any women over twenty-five in this country.[3] But at the moment she finds herself condemned by the canons of feminine beauty the mantis takes a second lease on life. Let the male escape her spells: the whole country is now hers. Her youth is dead? Long live youth and life! Life begins at forty. This is the age at which millions of Mrs Lippcotts, haunted by the thought of their vanished youths, close ranks and league together all over the country and take in hand its moral, religious, charitable, educational, artistic and

[1] Pastmaster of the art of understatement, the Major means 'much farther'. (P. D.)

[2] The first colonists found some wild dogs and pigeons on hand, but North America's only contribution to domestic animal life was the turkey.

[3] It is curious to note that a woman's 'ideal age' varies according to a regular progression from East to West across the globe. In America a woman reaches her physical prime from 18 to 25; in England from 25 to 30; in France from 28 to 40. It is true, of course, that older people in the U.S.A. enjoy a second youth. Thus, while children, wearing trousers, must ask their parents when they can put on shorts, sixty-year-old women wear dresses fit for young girls and have at their disposal the most formidable arsenal of rejuvenating weapons in the world.

society functions, maintaining their grip on them until their dying day.

Mrs Lippcott herself belongs to a good dozen associations: the Women's Christian Temperance Union, the local Knitting Club (weekly reunions from three to four on Fridays), the Schenectady League of Optimists, the Daughters of the American Revolution, the Sewing Circle, the Board of Advisers for the Social Register, the Baptist Women's Club, the T.T.K.,[1] to say nothing of golf clubs or bowling clubs.

I suppose there are no more easeful moments in Mrs Lippcott's life than these reunions where a good hundred smartly dressed, chattering, energetic women between fifty to sixty years congregate to hear their President call them 'girls', as though they were sixteen-year-olds: 'Now, girls, let's proceed to order!'—the order of the day being Mrs Merrimack's trip to Kenya, juvenile delinquency, the influence of Chippendale on American furniture, or the organization of a league to combat the erection of a bacchante in Boston.[2]

In my travels across the United States I have been struck by Mrs Lippcott's gift of ubiquity. Every lecturer must have been struck by the same thing. I set out to give a round of lectures on the Indian Royal Tiger (*felis elongatus*), and I come out of it with a weird feeling of hallucination. I no longer think of America as the land of skyscrapers, drugstores, ice-creams,

---

[1] Truth Through Knowledge, under whose auspices periodical meetings are organized where the lady members can listen to an account of a cruise or a mountain-climbing expedition while sewing or making pastry. Austin, Texas, boasts no less than 400 feminine associations. To make the Social Register, one must have two references from women whose husbands or sons already figure on the list.

[2] The reference is to the charming statue of a bacchante which the sculptor Frederic MacMonnies made in Paris and which the French government ordered a copy of for the Luxembourg Museum. It was originally intended to grace the court of Boston's Public Library; but the nudity of the dancing nymph, portrayed holding a child in one hand with a bunch of grapes in the other, was too shocking for New England's Puritan society, which, while not outlawing the pleasures of the flesh, forbids one to enjoy them. A meeting of the Patriotic Temperance League finally voted a resolution condemning this statue as 'an insult to the virtuous sentiments of Massachusett's' capital city' and requesting that this 'unmentionable thing' be destroyed. The unfortunate bacchante finally found a haven in New York's Metropolitan Museum. (P. D.)

Hollywood, the Pentagon and supermarkets; its symbol for me is the faces of three ladies, those three sexagenarian ladies, chirping like sparrows, who were on hand to meet me at the train or the airport in Des Moines and Omaha, Sioux City and Baltimore, Denver and Albuquerque—the President, the Vice-President and the Secretary of the Women's Club.

Everywhere they had the same tidy, spruce, carefully made-up faces. Everywhere the same welcoming smiles, the same sparkling teeth: 'So glad to meet you, Major!' Everywhere there were the same rose-pink straw-spangled dresses, the same blue satin toques with white petals, the same jingling bracelets. Everywhere they tendered the same little golden book to be signed. And everywhere they apologized for their husbands, who would have just loved to come, but unfortunately couldn't make it, either because they were held up at the office, or because they were dead—and sometimes both.

I haven't a doubt any more that it is these three ladies, reproduced in hundreds of thousands of samples, who really govern the United States. A strange vision indeed for my astonished English eyes! But I'm not at all sure that it isn't a vision that faithfully mirrors reality in this matriarchy where women's clubs have more influence on the White House than the alcohol distillers have on the French Chamber of Deputies.[1]

---

[1] This is to say nothing of certain states, like Vermont, where the inhabitants, who pride themselves on their origins, first ask a newcomer: 'Who was his mother?' as though the father didn't count. The matriarchal tendency in the United States goes back to the dim past. Among the Hopi Indians, who live 200 miles from the Grand Canyon on the plateau tops of desolate mountains, the matriachal system is still all-powerful. The house is the woman's property, and once he is married the man goes to work on land belonging to his wife.

THE PURSUIT OF HAPPINESS

 EVERY time our friend Cyrus B. Lippcott gets a chance to go to a football game and to plunge back into that 'old college spirit' he does so with irresistible exuberance. He sits down joyfully in the graduate section of the grandstand among his classmates of 1920, with whom he exchanges boisterous salutations: 'Hello, Jack! Hi, Cy!' He is overjoyed to greet them again just as he did thirty-five years ago, to celebrate the same sportive rites, to utter the same yells, to repeat the same gestures and to obey the same signals, given by the cheer-leader over a megaphone between repeated somersaults.

The Saturday I attended the Harvard–Yale game was a red-letter day for Cyrus. Harvard, his University, was going to win! For the occasion he was sporting a straw boater with a purple hatband and in his buttonhole he had stuck a huge red button proclaiming a defiant 'TO HELL WITH YALE'. At each new exploit of his fellow Harvard men he would leap to his feet, utter a war-cry, and then add a strident note to the prevailing uproar by blowing lustily on a trumpet.

Seated quietly beside him in the middle of 48,000 hysterical 'rooters' I had the strange feeling of being, by sole virtue of my composure, the last guardian of human dignity. Still, it was not the strange behaviour of the spectators that most astonished me. I was even more shocked by the way the referees were threatened by angry players, in keeping with those barbaric *mores* I had hitherto seen displayed only in France, and even then with lesser savagery.

During a lull in the game I said a few words about it to Lippcott, who took it rather badly.

'Oh, don't talk to me about your darned old cricket!' he said to me. 'The trouble with your players is that they're a bunch of introverts! If our boys didn't curse the referees, they'd be just like yours—full of frustrations.'

To see the demon of psychoanalysis pursue Lippcott right into the stadium is just too much for me. It's obviously no earthly use trying to argue with people in this hemisphere. Besides, how can you make heads or tails out of all these 'off tackle smashes' and 'end runs' where the ball simply disappears under great heaps of bodies? It did, at any rate, give Lippcott a golden opportunity to pay me back in my own coin for having one day tried to explain to him the niceties of cricket.

'Now if there's anything you don't understand,' he told me in almost the same words I had used to him, 'just ask me. I'm pretty darn sure I won't be able to explain it.'

And yet, good lord! it was at just this moment that we were linked together by the strongest of all bonds. For if there's one thing Englishmen and Americans share in common it's their love of sport and their undying affection for their old school.

Well, Harvard was winning. In fact, Harvard had won! This was one of the great days in Cyrus Lippcott's life! Going back on the train that was carrying him away from the joys of the collegiate back to those of the adult world, he blew more loudly than ever on his trumpet between generous slugs of whisky. And I couldn't help wondering if in real life he could ever have known moments when he was as blissful and as free to practise America's true religion—happiness—as in his college days.

For Latins in general, and for the French in particular, the notion of happiness is tainted with relativity. A millennial wisdom, handed down over the ages with other hereditary characteristics, teaches them from youth up that happiness is fleeting. 'Good year, lean year ... Where there's an up, there'll be a down! ... Life is short, so go to it! ... He who laughs on Friday will weep on Sunday!'—Such is the forest of melancholy refrains amid which the French child grows up.

It's a different story here, where happiness forms part of the programme of daily life. What am I saying? It was included from the beginning in the charter that launched the American ship of state. The United States is, I suppose, the only country

'HOW TO SUCCEED, ONLY 50 CENTS. . . .'

K 2

in the world which formally guarantees happiness to its nationals. The Declaration of Independence, carefully preserved under glass at the Library of Congress in Washington, ranks happiness among the inalienable rights of citizenship: life, liberty and the pursuit of happiness.

The pursuit of happiness! When an American is deprived of his happiness, he feels as unjustly hit as a Frenchman who's been deprived of his hunting licence. This doubtless explains why, when unhappy, he goes to consult one of those professors of human happiness who prescribe treatment for him with all the precision of a laryngologist.

An American has this notion of guaranteed happiness instilled in him from a tender age. In the Old World a child is treated to a daily diet of admonishments: 'Sit up straight!' 'Behave yourself!' 'Say "thank you"', 'Shut up!', 'Keep quiet!', 'Watch that elbow!', 'Finish what's on your plate!', 'Say "good morning" to the lady!' and between two cuffs on the ears he learns that life is made up of things one shouldn't do. The American child at the same age is stuffed full of ice-cream, popcorn, TV shows, vitamins, milk, fruit juice, music, toys and he grows up in an atmosphere of incredible freedom, where slaps, naughty boy's corners and dunce's caps are unknown. This is a world where the most frequently heard phrase is: 'How nice!' [1] It's a world where the only constraints are reserved for parents who must refrain from giving their children complexes by forcing them to act against their natures. It's where the young shoot must be allowed to give free expression to its personality. [2]

[1] Everything is *nice* even in prehistoric times. The caveman age, so grim for Europeans brought up on textbook lithographs of Stonehenge or the menhirs of Carnac, is presented to the American schoolboy in Technicolor. 'Today,' the text says in effect, 'is going to be a tough day for Mac Silex, caveman. His home was destroyed during the night by the Hercynian thrust. Where's he going to sleep tonight? He meets his cousin, Jo Miocenus. "Fine weather, Mac! How about going to hunt the septo-nasal mammoth?" They go off and after a terrible fight, they floor the monster. The mammoth's lair will provide Mac with a dreamy new home. And on the rock wall Mac begins to carve a bison. . . .'

[2] The Pochets were amazed at the number of left-handed people they encountered in the United States. Many write with their hands close to their bodies, with the elbow sticking out. This is usually due to the parents' reluctance to break the child of his habit if he begins to write that way.

I learned this to my cost one November day in Kansas City. I was watching some young ruffians splashing tar over a shop window when I got a cupful of whipped cream right in the moustache—all of it under the mocking eye of a policeman. I advanced on him, shaking my umbrella with indignation. Whereupon the 'cop' said:

'Don't you know it's Halloween?' And without paying further heed to the incident, he went on directing traffic with his white-gloved hand.

It was thus I learned, somewhat late in the day, that Halloween is the children's day of grace, when they can with impunity do anything they take it into their sweet heads to do. I couldn't help thinking, as I wiped my face, that America is decidedly a very different planet from England. Any further doubts I may have had on that score were dispelled that same day when I opened my latest copy of *The Times* (which had been following me faithfully around America). It told of how the headmasters of the county of Essex had just met and decided to limit beatings for undisciplined students to three blows of the cane and to restrict the use of the birch to certain particular offences.

It is when he gets to college that the American child finally attains the happiness he has been pursuing from birth. In these colleges he spends four years, sheltered from the harsh contingencies of life. Here he has 'dates' with the loveliest girls in the world while taking courses with professors who look as though they had just come from Hollywood. Cicero and fluid-drive, logic and rock an' roll, Xenophon at eleven and Barbara at five, anthropology and baseball, Kant and blue jeans, evenings spent in smoke-filled 'dens', the days spent sauntering across the grassy expanses of green campuses—all this is really paradise on earth.

I often wonder, therefore, how it comes about that Lippcott's fellow countrymen, and Lippcott himself, the most spoiled ex-children in the world, spend fortunes on psychiatrists and on the purchase of such happiness textbooks as *How to be happily married* or *How to get rid of your tensions*.

Emerging first from a world where all is permitted and then

from a collegiate paradise where all seems easy, the pampered young American runs headlong into the realities of life and realizes that the happiness promised him by the Declaration of Independence is not always easy of attainment. He cannot, however, complain of not being aided in his quest. The magazines, the films, the advertising posters and television attend his every step with a multicoloured theory of felicity. His thought is moulded by the syntax of happiness—that of the media of mass publicity. Life is served up to him on a platter as an uninterrupted series of sunny days; a paradise in which every car has that 'million-dollar look',[1] with a gear shift 'smooth as cream' propelling him as 'effortlessly as a cloud'; where all aeroplanes are 'luxurious', all women 'glamorous', all night clubs packed with 'charm' and 'excitement', all meals 'sumptuous', and where all trips are 'passports to happiness'—veritable magic carpets bathed in enchanted moonlight, where everything is fabulous, fashionable, rich, comfortable, brilliant, dazzling, lavish, princely, distinguished, exclusive, select, unique, of the period (no matter which), de luxe and has 'real class'; where everything is of a rosy hue, the colour of America itself.

There is always a touch of pink in the publicity posters. At the Lippcotts' everything that can stand a touch of rose has been brightened up with this colour or its variants, everything from crushed strawberry, tea-rose, old rose, to toothpaste pink and that baby pink which the old ladies like so much. Lippcott's three-tone car has a pink roof; his tie has pink stripes; Mrs Lippcott's gloves are pink, so are her hats and the linings of her coats. The sofas of their Schenectady house are pink, as are the table napkins, and the collar on their dog. Even many of the things the Lippcotts like to eat—sherbets, ice-creams, cakes— are pink. Even death has a rosy hue, since as everyone knows the morticians will see to it that Lippcott looks more rosy-cheeked than ever on the day of his death.

In this land where life, like death, is rosy-hued, Lippcott is

---

[1] The Southern Pacific Railway puts out a folder vaunting the luxury and comfort of the Portland–San Francisco streamliner, which it terms 'the million-dollar train with the million-dollar view'.

often haunted by a souvenir of the Old World, from the time, just after the liberation, when he was in Paris. It was at the Gare de Lyon one evening during the rush hour. The trains were packed with many passengers standing in the aisles. Seeing a *wagon-lit* sleeping-car next to a third-class carriage, a woman exclaimed: 'Isn't it a disgrace to see people who can stretch out and go to sleep while other passengers have to travel standing. I'd put 'em all in third, I would!'

This passing observation from an unknown woman left a sharper impression on Lippcott's mind than the smile of La Gioconda in the Louvre or the view from the Carrousel up the Champs Élysées. That somewhere in the civilized world a woman could dream of substituting third-class carriages for Pullmans is something he can't get over. It was a case he would, if he could, have taken to his psychoanalyst. Lippcott just can't envisage a world where happiness is thought of in terms of discomfort.

He is the proud citizen of a country where thousands of minds are employed every day in calculations intended to spare the citizen any effort—the number of steps needed to move from the sink to the refrigerator, the ideal height for beds so that they can be made up without fatigue, even bird-cages constructed so as to allow one to slip in a clean new tray (complete with simulated gravel) to replace the spotted one. What then must Lippcott think of people who consider a bathroom a luxury rather than a necessity? In a land where everything is based on making millions, how can Lippcott imagine that elsewhere millions might be suspect?

And how, good gracious! will my friend Daninos ever get Cyrus to understand that in order to be a leading politician in France, you must first of all be poor, or at any rate *faire pauvre* (appear poor)—the little house in the Vendée with its little garden, the slippers, the wood fire and the old cook all going to make up the stepping-stone to political immortality?

And yet I can't help wondering if good old Lippcott, who is the proud possessor of a vocabulary of happiness, a constitution of happiness, and the most gigantic assortment of happiness-producing gadgets in the world—*is* happy; and if he hasn't been running all his life after that happiness which his college made him taste for one brief instant.

For, generally speaking, Lippcott seems worried.

And what does Lippcott worry about?

About everything. About his wife, about his job, about the Stock Market, about the President's health, about death, about his vacation, about war—even about his hydramatic fluid-drive de luxe Cadillac, which might tomorrow be dethroned by an even more deluxized machine. If the United States is so overrun with experts writing books entitled *How to get rid of your worries*, it's because people have them on the brain.[1] A recent Gallup Poll reported that nine out of every ten Americans are a prey to preoccupations, anxieties, fears and even guilt complexes. 'Stop worrying! Relax and forget it!' they are exhorted from all sides. It's a funny thing . . . there's not a country in the world where people talk more about sex or where there is a greater display of 'sexy' pictures and sexual theories than the United States. Nor is there a country in the world where people talk more about relaxation, rest cures and happiness. And yet love and happiness seem more easily attained by a Normandy farmer or a San Gimignano cobbler than by Lippcott, for whom in fact happiness is one more worry.

Is Lippcott happy?

I would risk insulting his great country, which I both esteem and admire, were I to reply to the question myself. I prefer to leave the answer to his countrymen, in this case the editors of *Holiday*, self-styled 'the magazine of leisure for a richer life'.

'One of the great benefits of our system and our productivity,' writes the editorialist in a special number devoted to happiness,

---

[1] One of the latest of these manuals is called *How to Live 365 Days a Year*, by Dr John A. Schindler. 'Do you,' asks the author, 'want these 365 days to be an uninterrupted series, an exciting sequence of glorious minutes? . . . Do you want to skip joyously, enthusiastically and singing a gay air along the golden road of life? Of course, you do. . . . Well, the secret is to have "healthy emotions" and first of all to get rid of all excess worries. Begin today,' Dr Schindler advises, 'it's enough for you to say to yourself: from now on I'm going to behave serenely, calmly, joyfully. Well, all your stock of emotions will be renewed.'

'I'M VERY WORRIED ABOUT CYRUS . . . THE DOCTOR SAYS THAT OFFICE
AIR IS THE ONLY KIND THAT SUITS IIIM!'

'is the new sum of pleasures that they have brought our people. Hours have been added to each day, days to each week, golden years to each life. But the irony, the tragedy of this situation is that practically no one has learned to use this new amount of leisure! These golden hours only too often become empty hours. Very few of us really know what to do with the extra time which has been bequeathed us. . . .'

So, too, the late Bernard de Voto was forced to admit that 'the average American is ill at ease when he wants to relax. The qualities which proved indispensable in creating his standard of living become a tremendous handicap when he seeks to profit from his hard-won rest. . . .'

I couldn't have put it better myself, and I am much relieved that I didn't have to. But it's exactly what happens with Lippcott. Brought up on a religion of work, output and productivity, he is restless when he has nothing to do. The dismay he felt in Venice the day his organized tour programme indicated 'free morning' is only one symptom of this restlessness. *Far niente* is for him an unknown word, and it would need two at least to be translated into American.

As soon as there's no longer a button to be pushed, a handle to be turned, a trigger to be pressed, a pedal to be trodden on, a plan to be executed—in a word, something to do—Lippcott is disoriented. His greatest enemy is not the U.S.S.R.: it's solitude. Basically he would rather be face to face with a Russian than with himself. Radios, cars, television, films, gadgets, magazines are each day mass-produced and steadily perfected to fill his fear of the void. There is, of course, all the difference in the world between the desperate Russian who drowns himself in vodka and with a haggard eye turns to Aliovna Ivanovna and asks: 'Life, Aliovna Ivanovna, is life worth living?' and the melancholic American who can when feeling fed up always buy a Cadillac, or take a trip to Naples—and pay for it later.

Even at the risk of getting myself put down as a subversive by the F.B.I., I must say that there are more points in common between four Russians who retire to a room in the National Hotel in Moscow to drown themselves in vodka and four

Americans who decide: 'Let's go out and get drunk!' than there are between a Swiss and a Frenchman.

These two peoples love to drink: one of them to forget everything and to pose the big question, the other to stop thinking and to stop asking questions. Both are fond of group distractions, breaking records and collective efforts. Both are conscious of their individual weaknesses and the crushing power of their collectivities. Both live entirely for the future—even in daily life. (No woman can forget a night of love more quickly than an American.)

After all, the welfare of the world may lie in a well-planned marriage of whisky and vodka. And since one must respect that damnable French law of the triangle, let's throw in the *coq au vin* for good measure.

WITH POCHET IN A PLANE

WHENEVER I board an aeroplane, I always pray heaven to give me a neighbour who has never flown before. For this is the only kind of traveller who can't talk of his previous flight experiences. And one who smiles—a forced smile, sometimes, to give himself courage, but still a smile. I've begun to think, alas, that this species of traveller has vanished from the face of the globe. Usually I get veteran globe-trotters who look with an anxious eye at the chain of the Andes they have flown over twenty times and who give me a detailed description, as we are coming in to land, of how in 1937 they almost cracked up in Karachi trying to make a one-wheel landing.

The return trip from New York to Paris was in this respect worse than anything I had anticipated. For my neighbour was Pochet, and cursed be the destiny which made of Pochet (because he once piloted a Blériot back in 1934 and has friends in the aviation world) an aeronautical enthusiast and expert.

The moment we had finished testing the motors at the end of the runway I saw Pochet take out his chronometer and count the seconds.

'*Un . . . deux . . . trois . . . quatre . . .* mighty long getting off the ground,' he remarked. 'I admit that with these *machines* you have to check a hundred different things before the take-off, but still something must be wrong. We ought to be in the air already.'

We soon were, quite normally as far as I could see, and the plane began to gain height as most planes fortunately do. As we went into a slow bank Pochet started to tell me about air pockets and compared our plane's stability to that of another, far superior according to him.

'Besides,' he confided to me, 'they're soon going to scrap these *vieux taxis*.[1] *Je le sais* . . . I have a friend in the company. . . . Another ten trips at most, and all this *matériel* will be discarded.'

Shall I be frank? I don't much like getting into a plane that is making its first flight, but I like even less knowing it's on one of its last. Unlike Sonia, who's always on the *qui vive* ('Eh! don't you think the left engine's catching fire?'), I usually try not to notice all those little things on the wings which ooze, trickle, tremble and seem about to take off. This time I surprised myself by actually staring at them fixedly. Everything seemed to be holding together all right. We were soaring through space with swanlike ease when, half an hour later, I saw Pochet turn nervously in his seat and look at his watch again.

'I really don't know,' he said, 'what they're waiting for *pour faire leur changement de régime*.'[2]

I wondered why he didn't get up and go forward to the pilot's cabin to point out this oversight. This *changement* of the *régime* had me worried. One more thing I knew nothing about! How much happier I was before! Why change the *régime* when everything seemed to be going so smoothly? This damned Pochet was getting me all worked up. I imagined the drama up forward in the cockpit . . . the pilot struggling desperately with the controls . . . the engines refusing to slow down . . . the radio sending out S.O.S.s. I envied the young American couple just in front of us who, in the absence of an expert, had unfolded a map of Paris on their knees and were running their fingers across the Place de la Concorde as though they were there already. Ah, happy youth!

Suddenly the engines seemed to stall.

'That's it!' said Pochet.

'What?' I asked him, my throat in a knot.

'Why, the *changement de régime*! They certainly took their time!'

I breathed again. For several more hours, I must admit, my tyrant left me in peace. I would have stayed there, no doubt, if

[1] 'Old crates.'
[2] 'To change air speed', the change from climbing to cruising speed. (W. M. T.)

during the night we hadn't run into a storm (an exceptionally violent one, like all storms). I like a storm. I like the ocean. I like a plane. But I don't like all three at once. I said as much to Pochet, who had been awakened by the buffetings. But experts are like doctors: just get worried, and they reassure you; take things lightly and they get all het up.

'You are in a Faraday cage,' Pochet said. 'You have nothing to fear.'

'I understand,' I said, without understanding, 'but——'

'*Savez-vous*,' interrupted our technician (certain of my ignorance), 'that four planes in every hundred get struck by lightning without the passengers ever noticing it?'

I replied that for the moment I would rather get struck by something else. But already Pochet was telling me about his past storms, compared to which this one was just a *vulgaire pétard*.[1]

'Over the Sahara, in the middle of a night like this, I saw a ball of fire go right through the plane, what do you think of that?'

I said nothing, naturally.

'. . . It is all quite normal. Besides, as long as you do not see the hostess strolling casually up the aisle among the passengers for no good reason, you can be sure it is nothing serious.'

He had hardly uttered these words when the cabin door opened. Like a spectral apparition in the bluish penumbra, the hostess moved slowly towards us as though modelling a dress by Fath. I began to look around at the heads of my fellow passengers thinking they would be the last I would be given to see on this earth. They seemed sombre enough.

To while away the time still left to me and to think of something else, I picked up one of the attractive folders graciously placed at my disposal in the pouch in front of me. But luck was against me! The very first I took up was called *How to Ditch without a Hitch*. A charming reassuring little folder in colour which tells you just what steps to follow in order to land in mid-ocean 'with the grace and serenity of a seagull!' Being shipwrecked was made out to be such a picnic that it was positively

[1] 'a real dud.'

mouth-watering. The drawings, which showed the survivors playing cards under a parasol on their life-raft, struck me as being closer to Watteau's *Embarquement pour l'Île de Cythère* than to Géricault's *Radeau de la Méduse*. The text was no less sprightly. 'Your life-jacket, of a pretty yellow colour, and nicely tailored, can be found in a pocket up above your head. In case of ditching, remove all pointed objects to be found in your pockets; loosen your collar; remove your tie, take off your shoes, but don't undress any further. [I was already beginning to shiver.] You'll be that much warmer in the life-raft. Put on your life-jacket just as you would slip on a sweater and tie the upper string ends in a butterfly knot.' [There's at least one thing I'd forget to do in all this, another I wouldn't know how to—the butterfly knot—and a third I would do backwards.] 'Inflate your jacket when you are requested to do so. It is very easy. All you have to do is to give a sharp tug on the two lower strings. If the jacket does not inflate immediately' [so it's not that easy!] 'turn the end of the rubber tube in a clockwise direction.' (No folder is really instructive unless it mentions clocks somewhere along the line.) For the rest, there's nothing to worry about! 'All our planes carry an adequate supply of life-rafts, all of them equipped for maximum comfort: radio, fishing tackle and adjustable parasols. You now know all you need to know about ditching. Relax and enjoy your trip!'

I gave it a try, but without much luck. Seeing me awake, the charming hostess bent down towards me a strangely angelic looking face:

'Is there anything you need?'

'I've got everything,' I said, without adding that I had too much (thinking, despite myself, that if she could remove my neighbour I could die more peacefully).

After the hostess the captain came out of the cabin, followed by another officer, and then a third. So many people came out of the cabin that I wondered who could ever have stayed behind. The three men walked back to the rear of the plane as though the engines were in the tail. The simple fact that they had gone back to have a drink at the bar was, however, reassuring.

'They seem pretty young to me!' said Pochet.

Whereupon he painted such a portrait of the perfect pilot ('Still young but not too old, unmarried but still not too glamorous, full of sang-froid but not reckless, above all, a non-drinker, and a non-smoker too . . . but he must still like life sufficiently') that I judged such a man to be unfindable.

Meanwhile, to skirt the troubled zone, the plane began to climb in the night. It even seemed to me that we were climbing terribly.

'If this goes on,' I said to Pochet, trying to smile, 'we're going to end up in another world.'

But our expert was no longer in a joking mood. Pencil in hand, he was busy with mysterious calculations. I fell asleep. When I woke up it was already day. The Major, fully shaved, seemed in excellent spirits.

'Had a bit of a picnic last night, didn't we?' he cried, apparently delighted to have had a brush with the heavens.

Pochet, however, was still engrossed in his calculations.

'In five minutes, Major, unless I have made a mistake, you will see Finistère.'

I marvelled at his science when the coast came into sight. At that moment we were handed a sheet of paper: 'The city you are about to fly over is Bordeaux.'

'They must have changed course without my noticing it,' said Pochet.

Somewhat embarrassed, he didn't say another word until we reached Orly, where we landed as we had flown—without a hitch.

THE EARTH ISN'T *THAT* AT ALL!

(Translator's Epilogue)

THE Grand Tour is over. Everyone is satisfied. Martine is delighted to be back again in Paris by Nicholas's side.[1] New York, however, allowed her to *dégoter des tas de petites choses merveilleuses* [2] and to bring back several trunkfuls of those 'gadgets', whose sole purpose will be to dazzle her friends. The one exception is a little pocket vacuum cleaner, which she uses for every conceivable purpose—for removing specks of dust from my suits and even for springcleaning my moustache. It never would have occurred to me that an ex-officer of the Indian Army might one day be vacuum-cleaned by his wife, but this isn't the first time Frenchwomen have surprised me.

Madame Pochet, for her part, seems to have stripped the New York shops of countless articles in nylon, dacron and orlon that she just couldn't resist. Thus does the world witness a veritable peacetime pillage. For while the Pochets were pillaging the United States, the O'Connors were devastating Tuscany and carrying off all the silk and leather they could lay their hands on.

As for Pochet, he could not be happier! He has rediscovered France and its *cuisine*, and having now digested the U.S.A., he has stolen a long march on his friend Taupin, who can no longer browbeat him by waxing lyrical over the beauties of the Estoril. Both the Pochets, in fact, have come back shockingly Americanized, and expressions like *faire du shopping*, *le standing de la vie*, *Je vais check-uper*, and *avaler un snack* [3] are for ever on the

---

[1] A compromise solution was finally found for the problem of the Thompson boys' schooling. It was decided that the elder, Marc, should enter the Major's old school to receive a final lick of 'British polish', but Martine got her way with the younger, who is to remain in French hands up to the *baccalauréat*. (P. D.)

[2] 'to pick up masses of wonderful little things.'

[3] Mongrel phrases meaning 'go shopping', 'standard of living', 'I'll check up on it', and 'swallow a snack'.

tips of their tongues. They are even getting ready to send out
Christmas cards to all their friends signed 'Les Pochets'.

Ought I, for my part, to admit that I am a trifle relieved to be
back? I am definitely no more made for American life than the
Archbishop of Canterbury is for the Folies-Bergère. It's true
that I failed to get Martine to consider a prolonged sojourn in the
United Kingdom, but I have no doubt that she will one day
come to appreciate its subtle charms.

As for my friend Daninos, he has, I must say, kept his promise
in allowing me to get in a word here and there, and he has been
more than generous in letting me round off this book in proper
style. He also scored a point in getting me to say in my turn:
'England isn't *that* at all!'

Touché!

To think that Daninos had the misfortune the very first day to
stumble on a poor-quality Englishman who insisted on talking
of his stomach! How after that can I ever appear to him *digne de
foi*? [1] It's always the same story: in countries as rich in individuality as France, England or the United States, you have only to
enunciate some general rule to encounter its exception. In fact,
you encounter nothing but exceptions. The average Englishman,
the average American, the average Frenchman are abstract
creatures from the spectral kingdom of statistics. Pochet was
fundamentally right when he kept repeating to me: '*La France,
Major, ce n'est pas ça!*' [2] And so am I when I say to Daninos:
'England isn't that at all!'

A big country is never *that*! People are always saying: 'The
English, the French, the Americans . . .' But you have only to
meet one to be prevented from putting him in the plural. The
more a man resembles others, the more he considers it a point of
pride to be considered different. The odd thing, however, is that
no matter how many exceptions travellers may meet and bring
back with them from their trips, the popular images that peoples
have of each other are always composed of preconceived ideas—
so irritating for the nationals themselves.

When a country has won a name for itself because of its

[1] 'trustworthy.'   [2] 'France isn't *that* at all.'

'AND THAT'S OUR HOUSE; FROM THE SECOND-STOREY WINDOW YOU CAN
SEE THE WHITE HOUSE ON A CLEAR DAY'

Camembert, to the point where it means Camembert and nothing else to the foreign neophyte who visits it, Camembert begins to get under its skin. People exasperate the Swiss by talking their hind legs off about their watches, the Italians about their *pastas*, the Spaniards about their *toros*, and the Australians about their kangaroos. And why the devil do the French think they're doing me a favour by always seating me where there's a good draught? Are they themselves overjoyed when a young Yankee, the sparkle in his eye kindled by the Ville Lumière, gives them his definition of France: '*Gay Paree . . . Montmartre . . . la Tour Eiffel . . . les petites femmes . . . oh là là*'?

But there's no use battling against such ideas, each day mown down and each day deeper rooted. The Eiffel Tower, the Folies-Bergère, and the *oh là là* will always outshine the Descartes, the Pasteurs and all the Richelieus of France.

Tomorrow the Swiss could become the possessors of the richest uranium deposits on the globe, but the world would go on thinking of them as lactified and asepticized watchmakers who never leave a scrap of paper lying around. There's nothing like the Coldstream Guards' black busby and scarlet tunic for a British travel poster, and while there isn't one American in a thousand who lives in a skyscraper, the average Frenchman likes to imagine Mr Smith shaving (electrically) on the fifty-eighth floor of the Empire State Building. Now and again an enterprising globe-trotter will deliver a lecture to explain that Americans have a predilection for one-storey houses, never do more than fifty on the arterial roads, and travel in rather slow-moving trains—but the next day it will all have gone with the wind. A good Hollywood thriller sweeps away the pedestrian truth and with the aid of cars screaming through red lights and racing trains whose wailing sirens pierce the night, they quickly revive that postcard picture of America—the one everybody wants.

No, the entire earth is not that at all!

Yet this imaginary geography obliterates the other. This goes for places as well as people. Valparaiso may perfectly well be a port like any other, indeed less beautiful than many others. But it is Valparaiso. On those four magic syllables the dreaming schoolboy lets himself be rocked as on a hammock, his young head bent over the little dotted line that takes him to the other end of the globe (from Liverpool, twenty-five days). And this name will remain for all the Taupin Juniors of the earth that of the world's most beautiful port. And how can the Pochets themselves, after spanning so much ocean for the sake of such a name, freely admit that for one fleeting instant their hearts wavered between Valparaiso and Le Crotoy? [1] It's so hard, after journeying so far, to stick close to the truth!

Pochet, besides, can perfectly well travel all over the globe. But when one has been brought up in awe of English draughts, South African gold, Australian sheep, Argentine beef and Japanese hara-kiri, one's prefabricated geography does not abdicate easily before the original. For a long time Czecho-slovakia meant only a Hardtmuth pencil to me, and Brazil was a giant coffee-pot inlaid with sugared jewels. I had to see the people of Lima queuing up for the bus just as they do in Picca-dilly before the last Incas, in their gilt and gold, faded from the Peru I had carried with me in my head.

And yet have they really left it?

The more I travel the more lost I become, and the less sure I am of really knowing mankind. Perhaps discovery has three phases to it: a period of preconceived ideas; followed by the collapse of these fairytale realms; and finally, much later, the return to certain ideas which at bottom were not altogether false. . . . From the imaginary to the real, and from the real to the imaginary is all that is needed on this confounded planet to throw the most sure-footed explorer off his stride.

Does our planet even possess a centre of gravity? I have wondered about it for many years, but I now think I have dis-covered it at last. Yes, after a long quest, I have found the centre of the earth. Truth to tell, I had intended keeping this top secret to myself. But the moment has come to reveal it, as I earlier revealed the secret of the American Female.

No, my dear Pochet, the hub of the universe is not England,

[1] Small Northern French seaport in the Somme estuary. (W. M. T.)

happy as you would be to hear me claim it. Besides, everyone knows that England needs no introduction to the solar
system.

The middle of the planet, the centre of gravity of the world,
is not, as one might think, situated somewhere along the equator,
in the bowls of the earth.

It is neither New York, nor Paris either.

The centre of the world is Zanzibar, Rejkjavik, Sydney or
Istanbul. The centre of the world is where you are, for where
you are there will be planisphere maps, and the makers of planisphere maps always arrange to set their own country in the very
centre of the chart. The docile universe must bow.

One day behind the head of an important Swiss official in
Berne I perceived that Switzerland was located in the very centre
of the globe.

'Look,' he said to me, 'equidistant from Chicago and Peking,
the North Pole and Dakar, our country is really and truly the
centre of the world.'

The hazard of my peregrinations having subsequently taken
me to Bolivia, I noticed that the centre of the world had displaced
itself with me. On the immense wall-map serving to tapestry the
Bolivian minister's office, Sucre had become the heart of the
planet.

'Look,' he said to me. 'Equidistant from Paris and Vancouver,
Sydney and Moscow, Bolivia occupies a unique position in the
world.'

I looked. And for a moment I had the impression that the
universe was revolving around Sucre.

From Sucre, radiating out towards every azimuth, went
arrows, which seemed to diffuse over the world their beneficent
powers. Tucked away up in the right-hand corner, at the tip of
a tiny peninsula, France was accorded approximately the same
place which the schoolchildren of Limoges are used to giving
Kamchatka or the Aleutians.

Back in Paris I sought to reassure myself by opening Nicholas's
atlas to see just where France was.

Well, I found France again, a solid mauve block plumb in the centre of the double middle page. Paris at high noon, on meridian zero, equidistant from New York and Bombay, Greenland and Ethiopia, marvellously situated, like Sucre and Zanzibar: exactly in the centre of the globe!

Thus it is that the geographic sense is inculcated in the sweet heads of little Frenchmen, little Danes and little Zanzibarians.